Miller o

The Story of Chester Mills and Millers, their Trades and Wares, the Weir, the Water Engine and the Salmon

TEXT BY

ROY WILDING ©1997

In memory of Robert Bartlett of Handbridge

COVER ILLUSTRATION AND PUBLISHED BY
GORDON EMERY
27 Gladstone Road, Chester CH1 4BZ
01244 377955

PRINTED BY
REDWOOD BOOKS,
KENNET WAY, TROWBRIDGE, WILTSHIRE BA14 8RN

Mills of Dee *Detail from Aerial View of Chester 1855 Chromolithograph*
Courtesy of the Grosvenor Museum, Chester   *by John Mc Gahey*

Credits

Sharn Matthews (Museum Officer), Grosvenor Museum, Chester
Simon Warburton (Official Photographer), Grosvenor Museum, Chester
Mike Penney, Storm Photography (copyright photo on rear cover)
Steve and Philippa Howe, The Black and White Picture Place, Chester
John Morgan Fotoservices, 35 Willow Place, Connah`s Quay, CH5 4XP
Julie Edwards, Archaeologist, Chester Archaeology
Gordon Emery, (front cover and salmon illustrations)
Chester City Records Office
Cheshire County Records Office
Chester Public Library
University College Chester Library
Ironbridge Gorge Institute Library, Telford
Dr Brian Hodgson & Dr Ian Davidson, The Environment Agency, Buckley, Flint
Terry Kavanagh (Chester Local Historian)
Major Astle & Geoff Crump, Chester Military Museum
Mrs Tatler, The 'Ship Inn' Handbridge
Lynn Doylerush (Archive Officer), The Boat Museum, Ellesmere Port
Anthony & Hilary Thomas, The Northern Ceramics Society
Mr E. Royle, The Cheddleton Flint Mill Industrial Heritage Trust
Deborah S. Skinner (Senior Assistant Keeper of Ceramics), City Museum
Hanley, Stoke-on-Trent
Ann Ludford (Manager), Etruria Industrial Museum, Etruria, Stoke-on-Trent
Angela Lee (Presentations Officer), Gladstone Pottery Museum, Longton,
Stoke-on-Trent
Mr. Bob Jones, Sutton Hall Waterworks, North West Water
John Underwood (Information Librarian), The National Museum of Science &
Industry, London
Gail Cameron (Assistant Curator Paintings and Drawings) & Gavin Morgan (Photo
Librarian), Museum of London
Tobacco Manufacturers Association, London
J.S. Williams (City Archivist), Bristol Record Office
D.H. Hughes (Commercial Manager), Imperial Tobacco Limited (Liverpool Division)
A.D. Porter (Legal Manager), Imperial Tobacco Limited (Bristol)
Mr. George Jones (Director), Jones Diving & Marine Ltd., Northwich, Cheshire
Jo-Ann Gloger (Keeper of Collections), Forge Mill Needle Museum & Bordesley
Abbey Visitor Centre, Redditch, Worcs
Diana Smart, The Society for the Protection of Ancient Buildings, (Wind and
Watermill Section)
Mr Len Morgan (Local Historian)
Sandra Pane, Chester City Engineers (Drainage)
Chester City Engineers (Planning)
Wookey Hole Caves Ltd., Wookey Hole, Somerset
A. Lloyd Hughes (Archivist), Museum of Welsh Life, St. Fagans, Cardiff

Foreword

I was born in Handbridge in the middle of the 2nd World War. At the end of the 1950s, I worked for Albert Cheetham, a shoemaker, who was a shrewd little Manchester man. From nothing, he built a successful shoe shop and cobbler's business in Handbridge. Mr Cheetham was a great innovator who constructed a workshop from two concrete pre-fabricated garages bolted together, safely tucked against the low sandstone cliff of the old Roman quarry, just a few yards from the site of the old mills on the Handbridge side of the River Dee.

The stretch of the river contained between the weir and Old Dee Bridge, called the King's Pool, always fascinated me. Although I knew nothing of its history for many years, I was surprised to discover that this much neglected part of Chester was once one of the most important medieval and post-medieval industrial sites in Britain. The leather industry, situated here, played an integral role in Chester's commerce for hundreds of years, alongside corn milling, fulling and many other trades and activities which relied upon water power. The mills have long since disappeared. Nevertheless, with the help of many knowledgeable people, it has been possible to recreate the history of the Dee mills from Norman times to the present day.

The early 'Mills of Dee' consisted of the fulling mills at the south end of the causeway (weir) and the corn mills at the north end of the Dee Bridge. The name Dee Mills was more specifically used to denote the corn mills. However, this book includes the mills on both banks of the river.

Contents

The Miller of Dee

There was a jolly miller once
Lived on the River Dee;
He worked and sang from morn till night,
No Soul so blythe as he
And this the burthen of his song
for ever used to be -
"I care for nobody, no not I,
If nobody cares for me -

I live by the mill. She is to me
Like parent, child and wife;
I would not change my station, no
For any other in life.
No lawyer, surgeon or doct-or
E'er had a groat from me - and
I care for nobody, no not I,
If nobody cares for me."

Then, like the miller bold and free,
Let us rejoice and sing.
The days of youth were made for glee
And time is on the wing.
The song shall pass from me to thee
And round this jovial r-ing
And all in heart and voice agree
To sing, "Long live the King!"

From 'Love in a Village' (Oct. 1762), a pastiche opera
by Isaac Bickerstaff, Irish writer of songs and plays.

Owners and Occupiers

The Manorial Mills

Just south of Chester's city walls, the landscape of the River Dee is man-made. The Romans quarried deep into the soft red sandstone of the river bank. Centuries later, the Normans threw a great weir across the river and cut deep water channels to drive their corn-mills. The effect of these works on Chester was profound.

The weir was built diagonally across the Dee in 1093: the water diverted to provide power for a number of mills. The landscape was dramatically changed and the King's Pool was formed. The countryside for many miles above the weir was also greatly affected, because the water level was raised substantially increasing the risk of flooding.

The Old Dee Bridge dates back to Saxon times. The Domesday Book records that a hide and a half of city land lay *beyond the bridge,* but there was no mention of any mills at this time.1 The first reference to mills at Chester was in 1093, when Hugh Lupus, Earl of Chester, built the corn-mills of Chester and erected the causey (weir) in the Dee and granted three score fisheries, called stalls, above the weir to several of his dependants. Earl Hugh reserved to himself the fishing rights to the Earl's Pool (later King's Pool) below the weir. He granted the fishing rights and a charter for a mill *this side of the bridge* to the Abbot of St. Werburgh's Abbey.2

Shortly before 1119, Richard, the next Earl of Chester, re-granted his father's gifts to the abbey, with the notable additions of the Bache mill on the north side of the city and also a mill on the Handbridge or south side of the river:
I, Earl Richard, after the death of my father, have given, for the welfare of my soul (to the abbey) .... the mill of Bache....
*Item: the Earl Richard has given the tithes of the salmon fishery at the bridge and of a place of one mill on this side of the bridge: also the tithes to a mill beyond the bridge.*3

The function of the mill began to undergo a change as early as the 12th century. Wool was very much the staple industry of Britain but the cloth trade was also developing. According to Peter Wenham in his book 'Watermills' (1989), the first record of a mill being used for fulling, a vital process in cloth manufacture, occurred in 1168, and with in 50 years the tilt-hammers used in that process were being adapted to tanning.4 Richard Bennett asserts in his book 'Some Feudal Mills' (1904) that the mill on the Handbridge side of the river was subsequently and probably then (1119) a fulling mill.5 If Bennett is correct, then the Handbridge mill predates the earliest recorded fulling mill by some 50 years.

Under the Earls of Chester the mills of the Dee constituted the manorial mills of the city (except Northgate Street). The custom of Soke Rights was established, which Edward III reconfirmed in 1356. In later centuries, these customs were invariably recited in legal cases. Randolph Blunderville, sixth earl (1181-1232), seems specially to have placed the mills and their toll and other rights on a sound and satisfactory footing. So much so, that even as late as the 15th century, the customs of the *late Earl Randolphe* were quoted as good practice.6

Between 1232 and 1237, John le Scott, Earl of Chester, granted the tithe of certain new mills to the Abbey. Although this implies an increase in the number of mills, there is no indication to their exact number or use.7

Crown Property

In 1237, on the death of John le Scott, Edward, the first Prince of Wales, became the next Earl of Chester. Under his rule, the Dee Mills - now *King's mills* - became extensive and prosperous.8 In 1277, Richard the Engineer obtained a 12 year lease from the King for the mills and fishery of the Dee at a rent of £200.9 For several years in the 1280s, the mills, weir and salmon cages suffered extensive damage due to flood water and were put out of use for three months.10 In 1293, a inquest recorded the death of Richard Molendinarus, who was *killed with a cogg wheele of a milne of the abbots of Chester, which milne was leased from the King.*11

Richard Ingeniator (Engineer) was mayor of Chester in 1304, but it appears that he had no more connection with the mills. In 1321, Robert de Glasham was recorded as *farmer of the mills and bridge of Chester,* and in 1347, Bartholomew de Northworkyn was recorded as *farmer of the mills and fishery of the Dee for three years.* Pennant states that Edward the Black Prince granted the mills for life to Howell of Favyall, as a reward for his bravery at the battle of Poitiers.12 In 1335, the Walker or Fulling Mill, together with the Corn Mills, were leased to Richard de Capenhurst, six years later to Henry Russell, Edmund de Waterfall, David Russell, and Richard de Brocton for £210. In 1346, to Bartholomew de Norden at a rent of £243 6s. 8d. At some date after 1391, a new fulling mill was proposed, because in that year a lease was granted to William the Porter of Chester, Richard the White, William de Stretton, and Hugh the Walker, of a fulling mill about to be built on the Dee, for five years after the mill had been completed. 13

The year 1356 was a very important year for the mills at Chester, because the king (Edward III) then confirmed:
*by royal writ, as the recognised legal customs of Dee Mills, those usages which had already prevailed there time out of mind....*14

This 1356 royal writ was repeatedly cited in numerous seventeenth century lawsuits (see chapter on 'Soke Rights').

In 1356, the mills, including the fulling mills, were leased to four partners:

*Indenture of the lease of the Dee Mills, 29 Edward III., by the king to Robert de Bredon, parson of the church of St. Peter in Chester: Simon de Asewell, clerk: John de Newark, clerk: and Nicholas de Eccleston, carpenter: as well fulling mills as corn mills, with fishing on both sides of the bridge, but not the fishing under the bridge....The king granting timber from his woods and forests sufficient, by view of the foresters or carpenters, for wheels, coggs, rungs, sheldes, ladles, and other necessaries of timber....The king to make (rebuild) and sustain the causeway in the river.***15**

Also included in this indenture was a directive that the King's justice of Chester was to hold a yearly court in the mills. The mills appear to have prospered in the hands of the three clerics and the carpenter. The various King's receipts for timber from 'Delawere' Forest, indicate that the mills were kept in constant repair. In 1289, the rent for the mills and fishery paid by Richard the Engineer were £200 per annum. In 1356, the rent had fallen to £190. In 1377, however, it was increased to £240.**16**

In 1383, Matthew Haydock was *clerk of the mills, Chester, during the King's pleasure*, and in 1392, William Mareschal was *clerk of the mills of Dee for life*. In 1396, the Black Friars of Chester were made *tolfre and hoper free* at these mills. In 1400, this privilege was extended to the Camelite Friars of Chester, in response to their petition to Henry, Prince of Wales, that they were so impoverished by a recent *great murrain* and a raid committed in parts round about them that they *could not serve God or honestly live without aid.***17**

In 1394, internal trouble broke out in the mills. William de Wybunbury of Chester, Richard White, Henry de Felday, Richard de Hale, William Stretton, and William Porter, farmers of the fulling mills, petitioned the king to command the *stringent* observance of the covenances entered into by them. It appears that the servants of the these farmers were in the habit of frequenting the mills armed, thus endangering their fellow workmen. The servants were also accused of neglecting their work in the mills.**18**

Dishonest Millers

The charge of dishonesty was levelled against millers for centuries. The miller was allowed to take a toll, usually a sixteenth, of all the flour he produced. The question was, when is a sixteenth not a sixteenth? The problem stemmed from what Chaucer termed a miller's *thumb of gold*. Many things affect the density and content of corn, and no one possessed the necessary experience to judge how much flour the miller should take for his own 'ark' (bin). With experience, a miller could gauge the quality and condition of grain by testing it between thumb and forefinger. From this he judged how much flour could be produced. The complaint was that he regularly falsified the figure, allowing him, if Chaucer is to believed, to take three times his due. As a precaution, housewives were warned to *measure before and after* sending their corn to be ground, but this advice had little value. In an attempt to ease the problem, the right to make financial payment in lieu of tolls began to be accepted as early as the thirteenth century, although it was not placed on the Statute Book until 1796.**19**

In the 14th century, Chaucer wrote `The Canterbury Tales`, which has extensive and unflattering references to the miller. Geoffrey Chaucer, it appears, was reflecting a widely held view of millers when he presented one as a foul-mouthed, drunken churl during the telling of his own tale, and followed this by making the crooked miller of Trumpington, Simpkin the Swagger, a cuckolded butt of the Reeve's Tale.**20** Ill-feeling towards millers persisted for many years. The eighteenth-century Essex epitaph to a miller named Strange reads:

Here lies an honest miller
*And that is Strange.***21**

The millers sense of isolation was portrayed in the song of the miller of the Dee, written by Isaac Bickerstaff in 1762.

I care for nobody, no not I
*And nobody cares for me.***22**

John Walsh was the next lessee of the Dee Mills. In 1397, the corporation petitioned the king for a lease of the mills, declaring that a certain *John Walsh, also seeking the lease, proposes to use it in order that he might express his ill-will to the corporation by levying excessive tolls and extortion.* Their petition was refused and Walsh secured the mills. In 1400, Thomas Mostyn was the next lessee, and a series of alleged extortions and abuses were also brought against him.**23** Before the close of 1400, Henry de Strangeways became *clerk and keeper of the mills of Dee for life,* and he was succeeded in June, 1401, by Robert Castell as *clerk and approver.* His deputies were John, son of William de Lowe in 1407, and Robert del Hope who was installed as the manager of the mills in 1409, under guarantee of 12 years. **24**

There were internal disturbances at the mills in 1402-3, when Thomas Kydde struck John Brerewood with a staff, drawing blood. Brerewood countered the assault with a pole-axe which hit Kydde on the neck and felled him to the ground. On the same day Hugh the Walker struck David the Walker with an axe, and on the next day David returned the blow with a similar weapon.

Another instance of unrest at the mills was recorded in 1414-15, at the court of the Dee Mills, when Jown Kynsall, Walker, and Thomas Walker, servants of Ellen the Walker, were presented as being common wranglers and disturbers of the peace, who *came continually to the mills and created tumult and alarm among the millers and their servants.* **25**

Practical Men

In 1420-21, William del Moeles, former clerk and manager of the Dee Mills, was declared to owe arrears of £4 16s 9 1/2d In the same year, Richard de Hale and associates, the farmers of the fulling mills on the opposite side of the River

(Handbridge), owed £10 13s 4d In 1429, Thomas Butler, yeoman, had charge of the mills. In May 1436, Thomas Pulford, *valet of our chamber* (later *of our crown*), who had been appointed clerk and keeper by Henry VI during the royal pleasure, was reappointed for life. Towards the close of the same year William Foster is mentioned in the Minister's Accounts as clerk, apparently as the deputy of Pulford. In 1461, Richard Bold was clerk of the mills.**26** Pulford appears to have held the supervision of the mills for 28 years, and to have been succeeded by Randle (Richard) Bold, who was appointed for life in March 1461. By 1465, Bold was succeeded by David and William Malpas. In 1476, William Butler was made clerk of the mills by Edward IV, and was re-appointed for life by Richard III on his accession in 1483.

In May 1495, Henry VII appointed Richard Gough, and in November 1495, Richard Hanbury for life. Hanbury is said to have worked the mills by practical men, as had Robert Castell by del Hope.**27**

In 1498-9, the corn and fulling mills with the fishery were leased to Nicholas Hurleton.**28** In 1504, Hugh Hurleston, as *farmer of the Dee and of the king's pools*, was entered in the compotus of the king's receiver for Cheshire as paying on a 20 year's lease £50 per annum for the mills and £24 for the pools. The annual value of the mills and fishery in 1289 was £200, in 1356 it was £190 and in 1377 it had risen to £240. However, by 1504, it had decreased to the sum of £74 paid by Hurleston.**29** By 1507-8, the three fulling mills were leased for £11.**30** In 1509, the successors of Hanbury were William Poole, a member of the king's guards, and Edward ap John. These were followed by Hugh Goldsmith, on whose death in 1524, Urian Dymok, one of the sergeants of the city, was installed.**31** Bennett maintains in 'Some Feudal Mills' (1904) that the vicarious management of the clerks and keepers was inadequate to cope with the increasing difficulty of maintaining the ancient soke rights.**32** (See the chapter on 'Soke Rights'.)

In 1532, Henry VIII appointed Robert Brooke, who later transferred his interest in the mills to Ralphe and Thomas Goodman. According to Bennett, this was the start of a new era in the history of the mills. The Goodmans were practical business men, who restored the falling fortunes of the mills. The mills were enlarged, their resources greatly developed and concerted efforts made to restore the soke rights. As early as 1504, the Goodmans had been associated with the Chester mills, when Hamon Goodman, together with William Shawe and Roger Smyth had *farme ye fulling mille at xj.li per an.***33**

In 1553, Brook's 21 year lease expired, and Edward VI granted the mills with the fishery at Chester, to Sir Richard Cotton. Under the Goodmans the mills had prospered, the rental had risen from £74 in 1504 to £112 1s 2d, and Cotton quickly renewed the Goodman lease. By the end of 1553, the dean and chapter of St. Werburgh acquired the tithes of the mills, and leased them to Edward Plankey for £9 per annum.**34**

The Gamulls

In 1570, Ralph Goodman died, and his interest passed to William Goodman. William was several times mayor of Chester, and he died in his year of office in 1579. In 1583, Goodman's widow, Elizabeth, became the second wife of Alderman Edmund Gamull. In 1600, Gamull purchased the mills from the Cottons.**35**

In the same year, John Tyrer, a lay clerk in the Cathedral, built a tower above the Bridgegate. Water was raised from the Dee into a cistern at the top of the tower and fed through lead pipes and wooden troughs to most of the properties in the city. In 1601, Gamull became a partner of Tyrer, and agreed to supply water for power. In return, it was alleged, Tyrer agreed not to supply water to citizens who did not deal with the Dee Corn Mills.**36** (See the chapter on 'Soke Rights'.) In 1614, Thomas Gamull, Recorder of Chester, died two years before his father, Edmund. Edmund's heir was his grandson, Francis. In due course, Edward Whitby, also a Recorder of Chester, was appointed trustee of of the young Francis.**37** In 1634, Francis Gamull became mayor of Chester, and Whitby remained associated with the management of the mills.**38** Francis Gamull died in 1654.**39** The mills devolved to the five co-heiresses of Thomas Gamull, the father of Sir Francis. They were afterwards sub-divided. In 1698 a mortgage from Roger Comberbach and others to Mrs Locke states:

> *All that their Water Corn Milne commonly called by the name of the Moulding Milnes being one of the five Corn Milnes late the Inheritance of Sr Francis Gamul... and alsoe... a Malt Milne (& is the sixth Milne of the said Sr Francis Gamul)...in the possession of John Hopkins and John Hadley ...* **40**

The Wrenches

In 1742 and 1753 four-fifths of the property was purchased by Edward Wrench. His grandson purchased the remaining fifth share in 1808. The reserved rent by the Cotton family was purchased in 1776.**41** In 1747, Edward Wrench obtained permission from the corporation to add a new bolting mill at a rent of 12d. per year. This consent was followed three months later by the order:

> *That the lower window of Mr. Wrench's new bolting mill on the bridge be stopped up, it apprehended that the reflection of a candle light through the same at night will be dangerous to travellers on horseback.* **42**

A 'bolter' was a machine used in dressing or shifting flour, a task originally carried out by hand, using a temse. Temse was the medieval term for a hand-sieve; hence 'setting the temse on fire' for a good worker. Mechanical means were introduced in the 16th century, by flour being shaken through woven fabric fitted over a revolving cylinder. The fabric was originally wool, then calico and then silk.**43**

Disputed Ownership

In 1790, John Cooke wrote to Sir John Chetwode, of Oakley Hall, Staffordshire, disputing the Wrench family's right to ownership of the Dee Mills:

Whereas my father Tho. Cooke was a Staffordshire man who about the year 1706 had a lease from the honourable Lady Chetwode (whom I humbly presume was of your ancient family) for separate part of Chester Dee Mills, etc., for 99 years. Thus my father a miller came to Chester and occupied the mills under Lady Chetwode. In 1711 he married Mary Phillips, a farmer's daughter of Pooton (Poulton near Pulford) and he lived in much repute, well respected and in possession of the said mills until the time of his death. His death wound he received at his Wheat Mill by lifting up a mill-stone alone. This happened in December 1724. He left the whole of the mills and premises held under Lady Chetwode free from any debt or mortgage, to his said wife Mary and six children. He had two brothers who at the time of his illness were "undertakers of Madam Weston's mills" which were separate from those held by my father. My father then gave them a strict charge not to molest nor hinder his dear wife in the mills and to let his eldest son Thomas be brought up as a miller at the said mills. The two brothers, Tobias Cooke and John Cooke promised they would do all in their power to serve his wife.

Thereupon my father placed his hand in that of Tobias and said - "see ye to it, for if ye wrong my wife and children, there will be a black day for ye". My mother Mary and her eldest son Thomas were in possession of the said mills with a man under them during the winter quarter, but the said John Cooke got into his custody the lease to my father from Lady Chetwode. Later the said John illegally settled (at the time of his son John's marriage to a Liverpool woman) my father's mills &c. on the said John's wife and issue. After that my father's mills were illegally mortgaged to Mr Edwd. Wrench (deceased) about 42 years since. My father's mills remained unlawfully in the occupation of the present Mr Wrench until the sudden and surprising fire consumed the whole Mills. There now only remains, apart from the ground and streams, the wheel of my father's Wheat Mill and the wheel of the Shuling Mill [Shulling Mill - Malt or Meal Mill, mills for removing husks, from dialect to 'shull', 'shill': 'to shell, to husk'] which was saved by the ominous twirling round & flinging water out of the streams amidst the outrageous flames for their preservation which were a surprising sight to all beholders.

So, most honourable and gracious Sir, it is the most humble Petition of John Cooke (lame in both hands) son of the said Thomas Cooke, miller, and a Staffordshire man... that your gracious honour will be pleased to grant a line of the date of the lease from Lady Chetwode, the term of years, and the name of the man who pays the present yearly rent to your honourable house. Your honour's goodness is a great Charity... to the wronged and distressed. God will bless, and your most humble petitioner will ever pray &c. John Cooke...[44]

George Travis, Archdeacon of Chester, who acted on behalf of John Cooke, believed that he was an honest, industrious man who it was generally considered had been greatly wronged by a dishonest relation. Nevertheless, Chetwode claimed that he could find no evidence of Cooke's claim and there is no record of how the matter was concluded, but Wrench remained in control of the mills well into the 19th century.[45]

Handbridge Mills

It is not clear when the ownership of the Handbridge mills became separated from those on the city side. However, in a statement made in the reign of James I. (1602-25) it was asserted that there were three fulling mills held in farm by the Company of Clothworkers at a rent of £11 and employing 300 persons.**46** The number of people employed in the mills depended on the industry. Snuff-milling would not need many people, neither would saw-milling, but industries such as paper and parchment making, wash-leather working, felt making and cloth fulling would need many more hands. The water-wheel only provided the power for the ancillary work and the majority of the processing was independent of water power.**47** It may be that the Dee mills were among the earliest 'proto-factories'. The Chester industries harnessed energy, transformed by mechanical devices, to drive machines and also employed many people, in complicated processes in the manufacture of goods.

In 1600, John Tyrer may have acquired certain powers in the Handbridge mills, in his scheme for supplying the city with water. John Hopkins of Birmingham, ironmonger, and John Hadley, late of Worcester, and then Sutton Colefield, Gentleman, certainly did, in their joint venture to restore and improve the supply.**48** The southern (Handbridge) mills were mentioned in a conveyance of property at the Mills and Causeway dated 26 March, 1698, from Hopkins and Hadley to eight Chester gentlemen. This included the sale of the Lower Fulling Mill which had been converted into a Paper Mill, and adjoining the east side a mill called the Higher Fulling Mill, which was in the possesion of the Clothworkers and Walkers Company, and all other buildings, water, fishways, streams, floodgates, throughs, etc. belonging to the Lower Fulling Mill, and a third part of which was enjoyed in common with the Higher Fulling Mill and another fulling mill called the Mill by Itself.**49**

In 1699, Eleanor Panton of Chester, widow, sole daughter and heir of Elizabeth Lewis of Chester, widow, deceased, in consideration of £5 granted to William Francis of Chester, Gentleman (one of the eight grantees mentioned in Hopkins and Hadley's conveyance) her ninth part of the fulling mill called the mill by itself *which said part was commonly called one day's work in the said mill.* In 1716, Mary Francis of Chester, widow of William Francis (son of the above mentioned William Francis), in consideration of £630, released to John Tristram of Chester, apothecary, all her share in the property.**50** Six members of the Francis family were Chester postmasters from around 1580 to 1685. Four of these were also tanners. The last postmaster was William, who was described as *Alderman of the City, Merchant, Innholder and Postmaster.***51**

In a deed of 1776 relating to the water corn mills, the parties to the agreement were: Edward Wrench, John Glegg of Neston and Hugh Whishaw of Chester. Mention is also made of Edward Wrench's snuff mill, then under the holding of Thomas Moulson, and fishing rights in the King's Pool and the Cage (fish trap). Also included are other properties held, including Bridge Street, under the holding of John Bosley, Joseph Bage and John Johnson. In a deed of 1790 concerning the mills, are the names of Edward Ormmaney Wrench (Owner), William Orford (Miller), John Dickens (Carpenter) and William Evans (Needle Maker).**52** The Wrench family had an early association with the Skinners and Feltmakers' Company, for on April 1st. 1714, Mr. Peter Wrench was recorded as a steward of this company.**53**

The New Industries

It had been observed in 1814 that *in this city, although we mark the infancy of several manufactures, few arrive at maturity.***54** Two of the industries that did not survive for long were pottery and needle making.

In the mid-18th century, Randle Sorton established a pottery in Handbridge. However, it was isolated from the dynamic trade of the Potteries, and failed to make the necessary transition to high quality products.**55** Following the demise of the Handbridge pottery, William Sorton started needle making, probably using the redundant pottery's flint mill in the process of polishing needles. However, Chester appears to have had some association with the craft of needle making since at least the late 17th century, for Randle Holme, the Chester Herald, writing in the 'Academy of Armour' (1668) lists the range of needles available at that time.**56** In the deed of 1790, mentioned above, was included William Evans, Needle Maker. John G Rollins writes in 'The Needle Mills' (1970):

*...Needle-pointing on rapidly revolving grinding stones, scouring under heavy elm runners and polishing on buffs immediately suggest themselves as processes admirably suited for prime mover adoption. Some support may be gained for the idea from the fact that needle-makers settled themselves in communities in the vicinity of bridges, actually occupying properties on them in some cases. Examples are the needlemakers of Wilton, London and Chester; all had water-power available to them from mills either actually under the arches of the bridges themselves, as in the case of London Bridge, or adjacent to the bridge as at Chester....***57**

In 1781, William Sorton was a needle maker in Bridge Street.**58** However, in 1782, his address was in Handbridge.**59** In 1791-92, Wiliam Evans and Mrs Butler were needle makers in Handbridge.**60** In 1781, William Bage was a paper maker at the *Bridge,* Moulson and Eddowes were tobacconists in the Eastgate Row and J. & W. Nicholls were tobacconists and grocers in Watergate Street.**61** In 1782, Joseph Bage was a paper maker at the 'Bridge', Moulson and Eddowes tobacconists in Eastgate Street and J & W Nicholls tobacconist & grocers in Watergate Street. In addition, Thomas Nicholls was a tanner in Foregate Street. **62** In 1791-92, Mr Bozeley (Bosley) was a paper maker at the *Bridge.***63**

In 1789, the mills (on the bridge) were burnt down, and in 1790, Wrench obtained consent from the corporation to rebuild and *extend the mills upon the western side of the Dee Bridge on payment of five shillings, including the one shilling per annum now paid for the "previous liberty".* On August 3, 1807, the mills were advertised for sale in the 'Liverpool Advertiser', being then stated to contain *12 pairs of stones, six of which are French.***64**

In an article on the fire at the Handbridge snuff mills in 1806, the writer makes some interesting remarks about the mills:

*From time immemorial factories and similar works have been established on the southern banks of the Dee between the Causeway and the Old Bridge - tanning, skinning and barking, being all carried on there with varying success....some of them indeed to our present day. Each of them was governed by its own particular Guild or Company. One by one certain other trades allied themselves with those chartered ones, and among others, the Tobacco and Snuff Manufacturers, who had come to settle in the old city (in the 17th century) a quite new and popular industry. Some among the earliest tobacco-makers and tobacco-cutters were tanners and members of the Tanners' Company: which guild adopted the new recruits in order, probably, to prevent their seeking for incorporation as an independent body...two brothers Nicholls, who had been brought up as tanners, gave up their own occupation, rather early in the 18th century, purposely to embark in the already popular and profitable trade of tobacco-cutting: and while the Moulson family were not slow to follow them (the last in conjunction with the Croppers), the owners of both these long flourishing businesses competed amicably with each other on the southern side (Handbridge) of the Dee for the high reputation of the 'Chester Tobacco'.*65

The Nicholls' long association with the Handbridge mills was not only through tanning, tobacco and snuff. In 1630, Thomas Nicholl(s) was a fuller & clothworker, and part owner of the fulling mills.66

In 1818-19, the millers and corn dealers at the Dee Mills were recorded as: I A Frost, Charles Gamon and William Jones. Robert Topham was a tanner and skinner in Handbridge.67 In 1819, the Dee Mills burnt down again, and the Frosts decided to move their business to a converted cotton mill in Boughton by the canal. They used the relatively new technology of the steam engine for milling. The Frosts prospered in Steam Mill Street, and expanded the mills until they became one of the largest milling firms in the country.68

Hemingway remarks in his 'History of Chester' (1831), that:

*at the south side of the river (Handbridge), stood some extensive buildings; occupied by Messrs. Moulson and Cropper as snuff mills, by Mr. Topham as skinners' work-shops, some dwellings, and also a salmon cage. Hemingway states that some years ago, it (the mill) was purchased for £4,000 by the late Mr. Topham, whose son then possessed it in 1831.*69

The 1842 Tithe map shows the owner and occupiers of the Dee Mills (on the bridge). The owner was Edward Wrench and the occupiers were; Edward Moss and Messrs. Palin and Gamon. The 1842 Tithe map also shows Chester Waterworks & Warehouse, next to the Dee Mills on the bridge. These were owned by Chester Waterworks and occupied by *Themselves* and a Mr Palin.

The 1848 Tithe map shows the Handbridge Mills. The snuff & tobacco mill was owned by Edward Wrench, and occupied by Thomas Nicholls. The complex of: skinners yard & buildings, bark mill, tan yard and buildings, waste house, buildings etc., were owned and run by Thomas and William Topham. The salmon cage, bason and the road to cage were owned by Robert Topham, and run by Joseph Greenway.

In 1845, the Chester tobacconist, Thomas Nicholls, had taken over part of the snuff mill and land adjoining, and carried on the business of tobacco and snuff manufacture. After his death, the business was transferred to Harriet Nicholls, who traded under the name of Thomas Nicholls and Co. She retired from business in 1879, and assigned all her shares and interests in the mill and the land adjoining to her two sons, William Arthur Nicholls and George Frederick Nicholls. In 1889, the brothers entered into an agreement for the lease of the mill formerly belonging to the late Robert Topham, which they purchased in 1895.**70**

In Kelly's Directory for 1892, the Handbridge mills were referred to as the Deeside Mills. At this date they were occupied by *William Cattlewgh Jones, fell-monger and woolstapler, Martin Ebrahart - tripe dresser, Thomas Nicholls & Co, tobacco & snuff manufacturers and Mrs Hooley - candle manufacturer.* The Dee Mills (on the bridge), were occupied by *William Johnson, miller.***71** By 1902, the Deeside mills (Handbridge), were occupied only by *Thomas Nicholls & Co.* and by *Mrs. Hooley.* The Dee Mills (on the bridge) were occupied by *William Gregg, miller.***72** In 1906, *Nicholls & Co.* were the sole recorded occupiers of the Deeside (Handbridge) mills. The Dee Mills (on the bridge) were simply referred to as the *Dee Mills Co. millers.***73**

In 1911, H E E Peel of Overton and Sir H B Robertson of Llantysilio, two leading figures of the River Dee fisheries interest, who owned extensive fishing rights upstream, became the owners of the three mills (previously worked by William Catlewgh Jones and then Nicholls, Harriet Holley and Edward Jones & Sons, Tobacco Manufactures). Peel and Robertson also purchased the derelict Salmon Cage and Training Wall. In a 1913 covenant, it was stated that the Snuff Mills *had not been worked* for ten years.

William Arthur Nicholls died in 1922, and his share of the business was purchased by his brother for £42,350. 0s. 4d. In 1926-7, Thomas Nicholls & Co. consisted of George Frederick Nicholls, William Norman Nicholls and George Henry Grant. In 1935, George Frederick Nicholls died, and the Handbridge premises were assigned to William Norman Nicholls of Anglesey.

In 1954, Nicholls sold the Handbridge property to the Imperial Tobacco Company for £10,000. At this time the mills consisted of a two storey building and a single storey range adjacent. The total site area was 1,920 square yards. The Imperial Tobacco Company never occupied the building, and milling ceased in 1954. Twelve months later the property was sold to Chester Corporation for £8,500.**74**

Roller Mills

Hemingway states that the extensive property of the city mills (on the bridge) belonged to E. O. Wrench Esq, and that it had 22 pairs of stones. It was let chiefly, for grinding flour (implying that other types of works were carried out at the mill), to several tenants.[75] By 1860, Alderman William Johnson had become the miller, and he introduced rollers in the place of the ancient mill stone system.[76] The roller mill was generally introduced between 1850 and 1875. Large commercial mills, often operating near ports where imported grain was landed in increasing quantities became the accepted means of supplying an increased demand for the new 'white' bread.[77]

A major factor in the decline of the traditional mill was the introduction of hard winter wheats, developed in the United States, which proved difficult to grind using millstones. This cheap grain, introduced into Britain in the 1870s, was ground immediately on arrival at large commercial roller-mills centred in the docks.[78] Wenham comments in 'Watermills' (1989):

Only as new forms of energy - steam and electricity - were developed did the hitherto indispensable role of water-power begin to fade. To an increased degree, its limited survival in the 20th century depended, like that of the windmill, on a reluctance to consign it to history and not on strict commercial values.[79]

In April 1895, the Dee Mills were purchased by the corporation, only to burn down on May 29, 1895.[80] This fire considerably reduced the working area of the mill and the mill was closed down about 1898. There was a brief revival in 1902, when Messrs. Rigby, of Frodsham Mill, temporarily restarted the workable portions of the mill. As an experiment in the commercial use of the river, this firm carried a cargo of wheat in a Swedish vessel which was piloted to the mill wharf and successfully discharged. The experiment was not repeated, however, because the berth against the mill did not give sufficient depth of water for the vessel, which had to be moved to mid-chanel for several hours. This meant a loss of valuable time between the tidal high waters.[81]

In a 1913 covenant, it was stated that Chester City Council owned four Water Corn Mills collectively known as the Dee Mills, which were fed by 6 waterways or sluices. These mills were stated not to have been worked for the past 4 years, having been pulled down and *dismantled* and only the foundations remained. However, the Council still claimed the full rights to extract water for any mills which may be built on the site.

Hydroelectricity

Paradoxically, the increasing demand for electrical energy was to extend the use of water-power in Chester until the 1950s. Chester's original power station was erected in New Crane Street in 1895 and consisted of Direct Current Generators supplying a current at 210/420 volts. A dramatic increase in demand called for the installation of additional sets, and by 1910 the maximum capacity of Crane Street Works was reached. The possibilities of water power were investigated and in 1911 work started on the Hydro Station on the Old Dee Mills site (on the bridge). The new station contained three vertical Gordon water turbines and was officially opened in 1913.**82**

In 1913, the Council also installed pumps on the Dee Mills site (on the bridge), for lifting sewage from the south side of the river (Handbridge) to the north side (Chester City).

Following the Electricity Act of 1947, which nationalised electricity undertakings, the Hydro-electric Power Station was to be leased to the British Electricity Authority. However, the West Cheshire Water Order in 1950, authorised water pumping from the River Dee, and in 1951 the site was taken over by the West Cheshire Water Board, who leased it from the City Council in 1958. The Hydro Station was subsequently used as a water pumping station.**83** In 1974, approval was given for the installation of a river level recording station and a new penstock (sluice) wall at Deeside pumping station, Chester Weir.**84**

North West Water Authority continues to pump water, for both potable and non-potable use, to Sutton Hall Water Treatment Works at Ellesmere Port. In addition, the station continues to pump sewage from Handbridge.

In the 1960s, Chester City Council gave consent for the construction of residential properties, called *Salmon Leap*, on the site of the old Handbridge mills. In 1970, the installation of a migratory fish counter and barrier on the Handbridge 'island site' was agreed, together with an access footbridge. Throughout the following years, modifications and improvements continued to be made to the fish counting station and barrier. In 1973, approval was given for 'oversails' on the weir to *guide* the salmon through the counting station, in 1975 to a low concrete weir, and in 1988 to an extension to the fish trap building itself.**85**

Loss

With the construction of the weir and mills around 1093, the part of the River Dee called the *King's Pool* became the power-house and centre of industrial activity for Chester for 800 years. Activities included: grain, fulling, bark, paper, flint, needle and snuff mills, tobacco factory, salmon cages, water and sewage pumping, and a hydro-electric station. It seems curious that such an important industrial archaeological site, even though of the highest 'listing', has apparently attracted such little interest.

References

1. R. Bennett & J. Elton, 'Some Feudal Mills' (Wakefield: EP Publishing Ltd., 1975. First Pub. in 1904), p. 55.
2. ibid., p. 56.
3. ibid., p. 58.
4. P. Wenham, 'Watermills' (London: Robert Hale, 1989), p.22.
5. Bennett & Elton, 'Feudal Mills', p. 58.
6. ibid., p. 60.
7. 'The Causeway Mills in Handbridge', the 'Cheshire Sheaf' Vol. XXLIX, January 6,
8. Bennett & Elton, 'Feudal Mills', p. 60
9. ibid., p. 60.
10. W. Ayrton, 'Records relating to the River Dee and its fisheries', 'Journal of the Chester Archaeological Society', 6, 1849-55, p. 238.
11. Bennett & Elton, 'Feudal Mills', p. 59.
12. ibid., p. 65.
13. 'The Causeway Mills in Handbridge', 'Cheshire Sheaf' Vol. XLIX Jan 6, 1954, p 1
14. Bennett, 'Feudal Mills', p. 65.
15. ibid., p. 68.
16. ibid., p. 68.
17. ibid., pp. 68-69.
18. 'The Causeway Mills in Handbridge', 'Cheshire Sheaf' Vol XLIX Jan 6, 1954, p 1.
19. Wenham, 'Watermills', p. 21.
20. ibid., p. 32.
21. ibid., p. 33.
22. Wenham, 'Watermills' 33.
23. Bennett, 'Feudal Mills', pp. 69-70.
24. ibid., p. 77.
25. 'The Causeway Mills in Handbridge', 'Cheshire Sheaf', Vol. XLLIX, Jan 6, 1954, p. 1.
26. Bennett, 'Feudal Mills', p. 82.
27. ibid., p. 83.
28. 'The Causeway Mills in Handbridge', 'Cheshire Sheaf', Vol. XLIIX., January 5, 1954, p. 2
29. Bennett, 'Feudal Mills', pp. 83-84.
30. 'The Causeway Mills in Handbridge 'Cheshire Sheaf', Vol.XLIX., (1954)   p. 2.
31. Bennett, 'Feudal Mills', p. 83.
32. ibid., p. 84
33. ibid., p. 85.
34. ibid., p. 86.
35. ibid., p. 91.
36. ibid., p. 95
37. ibid., p. 107.
38. ibid., p. 111.
39. ibid., p. 122.
40 Chester Record Office. Roger Comberbach mortgage of 1698.
41 Hemingway, 'History of Chester' Vol.1 (Chester:1832), p.375.
42. Bennett, 'Feudal Mills', p. 123.
43. Wenham, 'Watermills', p. 225.
44. 'A Dee Mills Dispute', 'The Chester Sheaf', March 1949, pp. 12-13.
45. ibid., pp. 12-13
46. 'The Causeway Mills in Handbridge, 'Cheshire Sheaf' Vol. XLIX, Jan 5, p. 2.
47. W.H.Prentis, 'The Snuff-Mill Story' (Letchworth: Prentis,   1970), p. 133.
48. Hemingway, 'History of Chester, Vol. II, p. 239.
49. 'The Causeway Mills in Handbridge', 'Cheshire Sheaf', Vol. XLIX., Jan, 13, p. 3.
50. ibid., p. 3.
51. The Chester Post', 'Cheshire Life', Magazine, October 1961,   p.74
52. Cheshire County Records Office (C.C.R.O.), Deed, Ref. D/3589/1-6.
53. F. Simpson, 'Chester City Guilds: The Skinners and Feltmakers Company' 'Journal of the Chester Archaeological Society', New Series, Vol. 21. 1915, p. 84.
54. Wardle and Bentham, 'The Commercial Guide' (Manchester, 1814-1815), cited in J. Herson, 'Victorian Chester', edited by R. Swift (Liverpool University Press: Liverpool, 1996), p.16.
55. J and M. Hillis, 'The Chester Whiteware Manufactory', 'Northern Ceramics Society Journal', 4 (1980/1), 43, pp. 37-45.
56. J. G. Rollins, 'Needle Making' (Aylesbury: Shire, 1981), p. 15.
57. J.G. Rollins, 'The Needle Mills' (London: Society for the Protection of Ancient Buildings, 1970), p. 3.
58. Broster, 1781 Chester Guide and Directory, p. 102.
59. Broster, 1782 Chester Guide, p. 102.
60. Poole, 1791-92 Chester Directory and Guide. p.25 and p.27.
61. Broster, 1781 Chester Guide and Directory, pp. p. 101-102.
62. Broster, 1782 Guide, pp. 82 & 100-101.
63. Poole, 1791-92 Chester Directory and Guide, p. 25.
64. Bennett, 'Feudal Mills', p. 123.

65. 'Fire at the Snuff Mills, Chester', 'Cheshire Sheaf', Sept, 1885. pp. 258-259.

66. Chester City Record Office, (C.R.O.), Ref. X/Ch/1.

67. Pigot, Commercial Directory, 1818-19, pp. 103-104.

68. J. Tomlins, 'Victorian and Edwardian Chester' (Chester: Deesider, 1976), 'The River Dee' section.

69. Hemingway, 'History of Chester' (Chester: 1831), pp. 373 -379.

70. Environment Agency (Asiantaeth Yr Amgylchedd), Buckley, Unclassified papers relating to the Handbridge mills, 'The Causeway Mills', p. 4. (Courtesy of Dr. Brian Hodgson).

71. Kelly, Directory of Cheshire, 1892, p. 202.

72. Kelly, Directory of Cheshire, 1902, p. 224.

73. Kelly, Directory of Cheshire, 1906, p. 225.

74. Environment Agency, 'The Causeway Mills', p. 4.

75. Hemingway, 'History of Chester', pp. 373-379.

76. Bennett, 'Feudal Mills', p. 123.

77. Wenham, 'Watermills', p. 82.

78. ibid., p. 24.

79. Wenham, 'Watermills', p. 39.

80. Bennett, 'Feudal Mills', p. 123.

81. Chester Public Library, 'Studies in Local History No.5, Handbridge, G.R. Coppack, 'A Handbridge Miscellany', (Chester: 1964), p. 28.

82. Chester City Council, 'Electricity Undertaking' (Chester: 1946), p. 12.

83. Grosvenor Museum Display, Chester Hydro-Electric Works.

84. Chester City Record Office (C.R.O.), Refs: 4288 & 4458 B.Regs., TP 33/69 and 6/437.

85. ibid., TP.512 & 1304, 227/70 & 7/1/70 & 14598 B. Regs., 227/2/73, 6/1245 & 6/19398.

Dee Mills From Edgar's Field, Late 1890s

Frank Simpson
Courtesy: Grosvenor Museum

Soke Rights

Conflict

No matter caused more lasting conflict than 'soke rights'. Whoever owned a manorial mill in the Middle Ages had, and invariably enforced, these rights, which came to be bitterly resented by tenants. Soke rights were, in effect, a restrictive covenant giving the landowner the right that all corn grown on his land be milled at the manorial mill.1 Although soke rights never formed part of Statute Law, they survived for centuries, dying out only a hundred years ago. There were thousands of cases in Britain, and these were invariably resolved in favour of the landowner, to the fury of the tenants. Some of the tenants resorted to the most ingenious attempts to avoid conforming to the requirements. A not unusual ploy was for a group of tenants to build a new mill above the manorial mill, depriving it of water. The unsophisticated simply took their corn elsewhere and, when challenged, expressed surprise, ignorance or 'righteous anger'. If the manorial mill-owner's agents could be avoided, taking corn to another mill may have be advantageous, because competition was fierce and 'special offers' of reduced tariffs were commonplace.2

Reference to soke rights was invariably incorporated into leases. A late example was in 1871, when the town of Bradford was forced to buy a share in one of the town mills in order to obtain its release from soke duty. At first glance, the system of soke rights would appear to contain certain benefits for all. It was to the advantage of small communities to be self-sufficient, and poor transport limited opportunities to seek out alternatives, although the tenant did have the right to take his grain elsewhere if it was not ground within certain period of being presented at the mill.3

Although 'Modern' mills were more efficient than the old hand-quern or hand-mill, producing better quality flour with less waste, there were, however, two major disadvantages. First, because they were seen as a valuable asset, mills were increasingly built to last, and that made them expensive. Their upkeep added to costs, and these were, inevitably passed on. Second, farmers resisted the mill charges by continuing to use hand-querns until forced to give them up by law; even then many were buried to avoid them being confiscated, and they are still occasionally turned up by the plough. In some respects the second disadvantage was more important than the first. If relations between the miller and tenant had been good, soke rights may just have worked. However, relations were often hostile and the miller was often regarded as a rogue.4

Dee Mills

Under the Earls of Chester, the Dee Mills were constituted the manorial mills of the city and the customs of 'soke rights' were established, which in later centuries would be sited in many disputes. In 1279, Richard the Engineer was keeper of the mills, and Edward I tried to replace him by granting custody of the mills to his favourites, the

Abbey of Vale Royal. Edward was unsuccessful in removing Richard, but in another grant, he gave the abbey land in Bridge Street, leading directly to the mills, and also lands in the nearby precincts of the castle. The tenants of the Vale Royal land at Chester Castle refused to grind corn at mills. Richard claimed damages from the King who had introduced this element of discord into his soke district. An inquisition was formed which found in favour of Richard the Engineer:

*Inquisition held the same year: when it has been computed by the jurors that for the time the lord king has assigned his manorial lands of Chester Castle to the men of those parts in recompense for other lands assigned to the abbot and convent of Vale Royal, Richard the Engineer by loss of multure on grain of manorial tenants aforesaid which he should have received has sustained damage to the amount of 58s 7 1/2p. He is not able to assess future multure to them, however.*5

Up to the final year of Richard's lease of the mills, he had problems imposing the soke rights. In 1289, William Fox purchased bread at Warwick and brought it for sale in a cart at Chester, where Richard had him arrested and taken to Chester Castle. Fox brought an unsuccessful action against Richard, because it was ruled that Fox had acted in contravention of the soke rights of the mill.6

The year 1356 was important for Chester, because Edward III confirmed by royal writ, and recognised as legal, the customs of the Dee Mills, and those *usages* which had already prevailed there *time out of mind*. Every dwelling in the city had to grind their corn at the Dee Mills, and pay the lord the sixteenth vessel for toll. Certain persons were excluded from this toll, including the tenants of the abbey of St Werburgh. If any one used another mill to grind their corn, then on the first and second occasion, their corn would be forfeited to the *farmer* of the Dee Mills. On a third occasion, the corn and the horse that carried it would be forfeited to the lord the earl. No one in the city was allowed to have hand-mills in *prejudice of the lord's mills*. The many law-suits brought in the seventeenth century would cite this ruling as indisputable evidence.7

In 1402, a writ was issued for holding a court at the Dee Mills. This required an assembly of 24 jurors, who were to attend under pain of a fine of 6s 8d (1 mark). At about the same period, another writ was issued, this time under the seal of the County Palatine of Chester, directing the mayor and sheriffs of the city to announce the holding of a court at the mills to the king's justiciary and the chamberlain, and to provide a jury to *enquire as to an alleged offence of a tenant in withdrawing custom from the said mills*. (The chamberlain was a judge and the principal officer of Chester) The procedure was for the city officers, who had no authority within the mills, to issue a notice through the city that a court was to be held at the mills, and to summon a sufficient number of reputable citizens to make a jury.

In one particular case, William Dowell of Chester was found guilty of carrying forty-one bushels of wheat to be ground at Haffod Mill.8

The Corporation of Chester took exception to one miller, John Walsh, even before he had taken office. In 1397, the corporation petitioned the king for a lease of the mills, stating that a certain:

John Walsh, also seeking the lease, purposes to use it in order that he might express his ill-will to this corporation by levying excessive tolls and extortion.9

Their petition was refused, and Walsh secured the mills for himself. However, the allegation appears to have been correct. In 1398, King Richard came to the relief of his *pore leges*, and ordered that no more than the accustomed 16th rate of toll be taken for a period of four years. Although this term was probably for the duration of Walsh's lease, by 1400 he had vacated the mills. Despite Walsh's invidious record, he went on to become mayor in 1407 and again in 1411.

Thomas de Mostyn was the next lessee, and during his term the citizens seem to have rebelled and demanded an enquiry. They alleged that extortions and abuses which had been rampant *for forty years and more*, reached a peak under de Mostyn. An inquisition was held in 1400, at which amazing evidence of malpractices by the millers was produced. The jury found that Mostyn and his subordinates, like their predecessors, were guilty of extortions against the bakers, burgesses, brewers and *paupores*. The verdict was regarded as so important with regard to the true customs, usages and tolls of the mills, that as late as the reign of Queen Elizabeth I it was translated into English. The verdict had the desired effect, and by the end of 1400, de Mostyn and his henchmen had disappeared from the mills.10

The bakers of Chester were personally bound to grind their corn at the Dee Mills, which was formally made a condition on the incorporation of their company. However, in 1463, the mayor issued a charter which, duly recognised the bakers' rights and privileges, but ignored their responsibilities to the mills. When it was presented to Edward IV the following year for confirmation, the king *let them to wit* that their duty to the Dee Mills was not to be overlooked, and inserted a clause to that effect in his confirmation.11

In 1429, Thomas Butler, keeper of the mills, was accused of *divers transgressions*, and was ordered to appear before the court to answer these changes. In 1430, Butler was summoned no fewer than four times to appear before the court, but did not appear. No record of the final outcome can be found.12

In 1533, Raphe and Thomas Goodman, of the Dee Mills, brought an action against Thomas Thorneton, alderman of Chester:

On August 14, 24 Henry VIII., divers persons were bound for Thomas Thorneton that he should not carry any corn to be ground at any mills out of the franchises of Chester.13

In 1539, Richard Anyon and several others were also bound in recognisances that they should not *carrie cornes to any forren mylle*.14

Northgate Mills

The mills at Northgate, which, until the Dissolution, had belonged to the Abbey of St. Werburgh, had been worked by Thomas Bavand, who had been a sheriff of Chester in 1547. Bavand died, and his widow, Margaret, carried on the business. Thomas Bavand had ground corn for some citizens of Chester who should, under the soke, have used the Dee Mills. Bavand's widow, carried on this practice but the Goodmans took legal action against the widow and several others. She responded that the Goodmans had not objected to this practice when her husband lived. In 1567, proceedings started with a Bill of Indictment entered in the Exchequer Court at Chester by:

*Ralph and Thomas Goodman against Margaret Bavand, widow, occupier of one watermill, called the Bache Mill, without the Northgate (also of the windmill there); Robert Dandrey, esq., occupier of a windmill near Spittle, Boughton; Thomas Ball, occupier of a windmill at Christleton; John Moreton, occupying a watermill at Great Borrow; Philip Prince, occupying a watermill at Marford, each of whome, it was alleged, ground corn taken out of the city, to the prejudice of the Dee Mills...*15

The Goodmans pleaded that the late King Edward and his antecedents, the Earls of Chester, had always exercised the right to seize any forfeited corn carried out of the city to be ground at other mills than the Dee Mills, in accordance with ancient custom. All the defendants, except Margaret Bavand, do not appear to have offer any defence, allowing judgement to go by default or arranging for a withdrawal. Dandrey and Ball, in fact, appeared in evidence against her.16

Margaret Bavand pleaded that:

*Such a prescription in favour of Dee Mills is injurious and against the law; for that a prescriptive right cannot be in a matter of wrong.*17

The Court found against Bavand. She was ordered to *cease the carrying of corn or any malt of any citizen .. unto any mills without the same city, there to be ground...* In spite of this edict, the widow carried on business as usual. Three years later, in 1570, she was found *in contempt and breach of such order, still doth daily by her servants and assigns fetch and carry corn and malt out of the said city.* The Goodmans pleaded that Bavand's action was encouraging others to break the soke right. Margaret Bavand's contempt of court was proved and an order was issued against her in 1571. She was committed to Chester castle to be punished until she entered into bonds and sureties not to break the order. There is no further record of the widow Bavand. Bennett comments in 'Some Feudal Mills' (1904), that her desperate attempt to earn a living for herself and her family at the expense of the Dee Mills proved so *utter a futility.* 18

Horse-mill

In 1583, Alderman Edmund Gamull began the task of protecting the trade of the mills by taking action against his old colleague, Alderman John Hankey, ex-mayor of Chester. Public allegations had once again been made that the Dee millers were practising extortion. These allegations were supported by Hankey, who set up a horse-mill *for the welfare of the community, and ground for the citizens at the proper rate of 1/16th*. In 1567, Hankey had showed his *public spirit* when he co-operated with the mayor of Chester in suppressing *the great strike* of the city bakers, which had threatened to starve the city.

Gamull's action against Hankey was for erecting a horse-mill and withdrawing his own and others' grist from the Dee Mills. Hankey made a strong case of extortion against the soke-millers, and a rider attached to a court order of 1585 revealed a strong sympathy with the defendant (Hankey). The decision of the court was that the Dee millers should not take more than the ancient toll for grinding. Also, as the defendant (Hankey) had incurred costs erecting the horse-mill, the court decided that the mill should remain for Hankey's lifetime, and Hankey either pay a yearly rent on the horse-mill to the Dee Mills, or the Dee Mills buy Hankey out.[19]

In Bennett's opinion, with this decision, the Dee soke was practically broken. The mere idea of buying out the builder of an illegal mill, or compensating him for his expenses in resisting ancient custom, saw the beginning of the end of the soke. There is no record of the arrangement made with Hankey, but he had gained a great victory at considerable risk to himself. As to Gamull, he went on to erect a new mill at the Dee mills (on the bridge) in preparation for an increase in business and, in 1586, he became mayor of Chester.[20]

In 1620 the City Treasurer recorded dues for a *horssemill at Cowlane end 2s.*[21]

Corn and Water

There were many more recorded cases of dissension over the soke and the questionable way the Dee millers conducted business. However, perhaps a unique occurrence in the history of British watermills was the alliance, in 1601, between Edmund Gamull and John Tyrer. In order to enforce the soke rights in Chester, Gamull became a partner in Tyrer's waterworks next to the Dee Mills (on the bridge). It was alleged that Tyrer agreed not to supply water to any citizens who refused to grind their corn at the Dee Mills. Gamull's and Tyrer's actions were to incite some citizens of Chester and other interested parties upstream of the Dee Mills to demand the demolition of the weir, thus depriving both the mills and waterworks of power and water and freeing them from the soke for ever.[22] However, the weir was not removed. (The proceedings of this dispute will be discussed in the 'Threats and Changes' chapter).

The alliance of the mill with Tyrer's waterworks continued from 1601, the time of Edmund Gamull, with Tyrer faithfully carrying out his part of the bargain in refusing water from his pumping-works to absentees from the mills. In 1634, Tyrer died and his son opened up negotiations for the sale of the waterworks to Francis Gamull. About this time Randle Holmes petitioned Gamull, then mayor, that the waterworks were charging greater rents than before, and had wrongfully cut off the service-pipes to city properties.

It appears that others were interested in the purchase of the coercive milling factor; and during Gamull's absence from Chester the waterworks were acquired in the *'public interest'* by Sir R. Mainwaring, ex-alderman of Chester, and friends. **23** The agreement was that purchasers should pay the owners of the Dee Mills a rental of £10 per annum on a lease of ten years. However, Mainwaring and his partners cut the tie that bound the waterworks to the Dee Mills and, of course, Gamull took legal action against them, which finally reached the Star Chamber in 1635. It was held that the owners of the waterworks were entitled to receive their supply from the mill-pool on payment of the old rent. However, the crux of the matter, whether they should force their customers to grind at the Dee Mills, was left for the Court of Exchequer to decide, There does not appear to be a record of this decision, but it was apparently adverse to Gamull, because no more was heard of the old standing alliance between the waterworks and the Dee Mills.**24**

Windmills

In 1729/30, the Company of Bakers petitioned the Chester Assembly complaining of *impositions and grievances* relating to the Dee Mills within the city. The Assembly gave permission for the bakers to erect two windmills in Hough Green:

> *ordered that they might have a grant in fee-farm of the ground desired, being '50 yards' square on Hough Green near Brewers Hallgate and '100 yards' long by '50 yards' on the Red hill there as they were staked out, in order to erect windmills and to have liberty to get clay in the said ground or as near there as it be got. They were to fill up, level and make good the ground as it was, paying 'ten shillings' per annum rent for each mill, with proper covenants for erecting two good windmills and maintaining and keeping the same in good repair and not to take above a 'toll dish', containing no more than four pounds heaped for the grinding of every measure of corn, and to be used to work the mills and not to convert the ground to any other use...* **25**

The Cestrian`s Lot

In conclusion, similar to conditions over other parts of England and Wales, the relations between millers and citizens at Chester over the ages were often very hostile. Under the soke rights, Cestrians were made to grind their corn at the Dee Mills, often at extortionate rates. However, unlike smaller country mills, Chester millers did not have matters all their own way, and they encountered formidable opposition from astute businessmen like Aldermen Hankey and Mainwairing.

Stone Quern

References

1. Wenham, 'Watermills', p. 20.
2. ibid., p. 20.
3. ibid., pp. 20-21.
4. ibid., p. 21.
5. Bennett, 'Feudal Mills', p. 62.
6. ibid., p. 63.
7   ibid., p. 65.
8. ibid., p. 66.
9. ibid., p. 70.
10. Harleian MSS. 2083.517 in Bennett, 'Feudal Mills', pp. 70 -76.
11. Harleian MSS. 2054.41-45. in Bennett, 'Feudal Mills', pp. 78 -81.
12. Bennett, 'Feudal Mills', p. 82.
13. ibid., p. 85.
14. ibid., p. 85.
15. ibid., p. 87.
16. ibid., p. 87.
17. ibid., p. 89.
18. ibid., p. 91.
19. ibid., p. 93.
20. ibid., p. 94.
21 C.R.O. Treasurer's Accounts TAR/ 2/38
22 Bennett, `Feudal Mills`, p 95
23 ibid., p. 112.
24. ibid., p. 113.
25. Chester Record Office, Assembly Book, A/B/4, 1729-30, p29.

Corn Hand Mill

Threats and Changes

Human Factors

Early in the 17th century, a Commission of Sewers was appointed to investigate specific instances of flooding or poor drainage. The Commission was empowered to clear obstructions that impeded the clear flow of the river. In 1607 or 1608, a Commission was granted for the removal of obstructions in the Dee, both to prevent flooding and improve navigation. Evidence was given that the weirs at Chester (stone) and Eaton (wooden) harmed navigation, caused flooding, and hindered migratory fish. The Commission concluded that floods caused by the two weirs did damage land, *to the value of £300 per annum.* Accordingly, it was decreed that one third of the Eaton weir should be removed, and that a *10 yard* length of the Chester weir *in the middle of the channel, down to the bottom of the river, shall be pulled down and taken away.* On appeal, this ruling was overturned, on the grounds that weirs erected before the reign of Edward 1, and not enhanced since then, were exempt from the actions of any Commission of Sewers. In June 1609, the Privy Council quashed the decree, and forebade the Commissioners to carry out their original intent. Chester Weir survived, although there were further unsuccessful attempts at its removal in 1646-48. Eaton Weir was dismantled sometime before 1693.[1]

In 1840, Robert Stevenson and Sons, consulting civil engineers, reported on the problem of flooding on low-lying land in the neighbourhood of Eaton Hall. The report stated unequivocally that the chief cause of the floods was Chester Weir. The weir raised the river by 3.5 metres above its natural level, thereby affecting the flow for seven miles upstream. One of the solutions proposed was to lower the level of the weir temporarily at the onset of floods. However, due to the height of the weir, and its construction, this could only be attempted on a limited scale and with limited results. Having rejected all other proposals, the report recommended the removal of Chester Weir as *the only remedy for the floodings of the Dee.* Failing this, lowering its level by nothing short of at least 1.5 metres for its full length would prevent the flooding at Eaton. The report acknowledged that this action would affect the rights of the Dee Mills, and concluded that it would be necessary either to acquire the mills outright, or provide compensation.[2]

Section 42 of the 1865 Salmon Fishery Act required owners of mill dams or weirs to provide for the safe passage of fish around their structures. In 1869, a Court of Inquiry was held *with respect to the removal of such fishing weirs, or fixed engines, or the alterations of such fishing mill dams [at] the Dee Mills.* At the southern end of Chester Weir lay the Handbridge Snuff Mills, and fixed across their tailrace was an *inoperative* ancient salmon cage, at least 300 years old, for catching fish, but which served the function of a fish pass in the weir. Both the Fishery Board, and the owner of the snuff mills, wished to replace the cage with a purpose-built fish pass. This proposal was opposed by the owners of the Dee Mills, at the opposite end of the weir, who claimed that it would divert water away from their establishment. At the inquiry it was agreed to remove the cage, but leave the mill race as it was for an experimental period. If it proved unsatisfactory, a new fish pass would be constructed. Nearly forty years later, the Board prepared evidence on the current state of the fisheries. It reported that there were five mills on the River Dee, all with fish passes, with the exception of Chester. A fish pass at Chester was proposed again in 1911, and had been constructed by 1914, by lowering a crest of the weir.

In 1888, The Medical Officer of Health for Chester reported that during the past two years, Chester had experienced excessive mortality from enteric fever. As a consequence, the local Government Board instructed the Medical Officer of Health to investigate the causes of the outbreak, and suggest ways of preventing any future occurrence. The Medical Officer reported that raw sewage discharged into the river contained the contagium of enteric fever. Chester Waterworks Company's intake was on the south side of the river above Chester Weir, but the high tides brought the raw sewage back over the weir. Between low water and the time when the tide began to rise, the water between Saltney and Chester Weir was nearly stagnant and filled with raw sewage.

In 1894, the Corporation Water Supply Committee published in a report that a proper interceptive sewer for the south side of the city be provided, and to the erection of sluices in or near to the present weir, similar to those erected across the Thames at Richmond, which would prevent the tide rising over the weir.

In 1895, the concept was developed at length by Ransomes and Rapier. The sluices were to be about two metres higher than the present causeway (weir) to regulate the incoming tide. The sill of the sluices would be placed about two metres lower than the present causeway, giving a freer discharge to prevent upstream flooding. Part of the causeway butting onto the bridge was to be raised, while the rest of it would be demolished. Because the sluices were intended to replace the existing weir, the Corporation acquired the Dee Mills and Weir in 1895.

In 1895, Chester Corporation resolved *to apply to Parliament in the ensuing session for an Act authorising the construction of Sluices near the Weir.* Altogether, there were 22 petitions against the Bill, and after detailed consideration by a House of Commons Select Committee, it was rejected. In preparation for the Sluices Bill, Chester Corporation had already purchased the Dee Mill (on the bridge) and associated water rights in April 1895. One month later, the mills were wrecked by fire. In 1910, The Corporation decided to demolish the mills to the level of the Dee Bridge. It was then that S E Britton, the City Electrical Engineer, suggested using available power for generation. In 1912, a public enquiry was held to seek authorisation for the scheme from the Local Government Board. The Corporation proposed to increase the mean height of the weir by *7.25 inches.* This proposal faced strong opposition from bodies like the Dee Fisheries Board and Dee Conservancy Board.

The Fire at Dee Mills, 1895   *Courtesy of Steve Howe*

Faced with this opposition, the Corporation withdrew its proposal to raise the weir. However, in 1915, Chester Corporation and the Waterworks Company proposed that the height of the weir be increased by *12 inches*. This time, the Board of Agriculture and Fisheries "reluctantly" accorded to the request, on the understanding that *the measure is temporary, and it will be reduced 12 inches after the War*. The weir was duly raised, but not lowered to its original height until May 1922.

The Hydro-electric Power Station was opened in 1913. The generating building, the retaining wall between it and the Dee Bridge, and 37 metres of river wall below the weir, were all built of concrete, and faced with sandstone masonry taken from the foundations of the old mills.3

Ice, Fire, Floods and War

By the 13th century, the Dee Mills had been acquired by the Crown, and in 1277, they were leased for a term of 12 years to Edward 1's engineer, Master Richard, together with his fisheries in the water of Dee, belonging to the *Bridge over that water*. At the expiration of the lease, Richard successfully claimed compensation for damage caused to the mills, and the causeway or weir, by *frequently occuring inundations* of the river. An inquisition found that in the first year of Richard the engineer's lease, so many inundations of water had frequently arisen, whilst Richard remained on the King's service at Caernarvon, that it had not been possible to set the fish traps (crates) under the bridge, and the fishing pools and granaries together with the walls of the mills, had been thrown down and carried away. Also, for the three following years, whilst Richard was serving his King in the Welsh Wars, flood water dispersed the pools and traps, together with the causeway. In addition, when Richard was serving the King at Trosselan, the causeway remained *thrown down and carried away,* and the mills could not be worked for almost three months. In fact, for almost the whole term of Richard's lease the mills often remained out of action.

In 1356, a lease for the mills bound the Crown to maintain the Weir, *and if the said causeway be damaged by misfortune, or rage of water, the leases not to be chargeable with the damage.* On 5th February 1601, a great part of the causeway broke down, and put the mills out of action until the following May. **4** The Gamulls were reported to have *expended a large sum in repairing the causeway...***5**

In the winter of 1606-7, there was *a greate frost that continued from Michaelmas to the middest of February.* For miles round the small rural mills were frozen into silence. However, the Dee Mills were not affected and continued to operate. The fact that the Dee Mills continued working, while others were still, was taken advantage of by Edmund Gamull and his associates. John Wilding and Richard Primatt, both of Chester, recorded the following on a visit to Marford mill:

Memo. That upon the xij [12th] daye of January they whose names bee subscribed, having beene upon occasion at Wrixham, in theyr returne they came by Sir Richard Trevor his milles at Marford, being in the highe waie side and about iiij miles from Chester: And because they saw the said milles standing still and not gryding, Richard Prymatt, one of theym who subscribes, took occasion to questyon with the millner of the sayde milles and asked him the cause wherefore they wroughte not. Who answered him that all the saide milles (being iiij in number) had not wrought for 5 or 6 daies then past; And the cause thereof was the froste. Then the said Richard Prymatt asked him wherefore they could not have broken and thawed the froste by some devise or meanes. Who answered him it wold doe noeggod, for they wanted water to serve theym withall. And then the said Richard asked him howe they wold doe upon the like occasion of want, yf Chester milles went downe: he answered he could not tell howe they shold doe. But how longe after the said milles stood by the meanes above saied they cannot declare. All of which they will be ready to depose as occasion shall require.

*Ric. Primate and John Wildinge.***6**

Sir Richard Trevor, the owner of Marford Mill, was the leader of the hostile movement to the Dee Mills, and the group calling for the demolition of the Chester weir. Trevor was hostile towards the Chester mills because he argued that the Chester Weir caused flooding to his land. Also, with the removal of the Chester soke, his Marford mill would attract more business. Weirs have always been the cause of constant conflict over the ages, either by depriving water to land below it or causing flooding above it. The 19th century novelist, George Elliot (Mary Ann Evans), described just such a conflict in her book 'The Mill on the Floss' (1860).

During the siege of Chester, which began in 1644, and lasted until the city's surrender in February 1646, Randle Holmes recorded that the long street called Handbridge with all the lanes, barns and buildings about it, including the fullers or Walkers mills were:
*ruinated and burnt to the ground by the Parliament forces and when a great part of them had been rebuilt, they were again burnt down by the same army.***7**

Quite apart from the Civil War damage, *divers breaches* were made in the *causey* in the late 1640s, in an unsuccessful attempt to improve the navigation of the Dee.**8** Moreover, an old Chester tradition had it that some uninscribed tombstones were taken from the ruins of an ancient chapel in Edgar's Field, Handbridge around that time *to mend a breach in the fishery dam across the weir: but whilst one stone remained therein, the dam could not be kept up.***9**

In 1649, Chester Assembly issued an order to Arthur Harvie for sluices in the weir:
*...that the city should make a lease for one year beginning at Michaelmas next to Arthur Harvie or any other who should make such sluices as would suffice to cleanse the river...***10**
However, no sluices appear to have been made.

There were many fires at the Chester mills. Prior to the introduction of metal stanchions and beams, wooden beams and flooring were used in the construction of mill buildings. Excessive heat was generated by kilns used for drying oats and tobacco leaves, and the mills were lit by candles or lamps. In addition, the dry

Derelict Mills After The Fire, 1910   *From a painting by Campbell G Walker*
Courtesy of the Grosvenor Museum

atmosphere of mills made them susceptible to fire. The corn mills (on the bridge) were burnt down in 1789, 1819, 1847 and for a fourth and final time in 1895.**11** The fire in 1819 was probably caused by excessive heat from a kiln used for drying oaks for making meal. During this fire, one poor man was *burned to a cinder.***12** Fires were also recorded at the Handbridge Snuff Mills in 1701, 1806 and 1950s. The fire in 1701 started early one Saturday morning in the snuff mill owned by Mr Thomas Topham, when it was reported that *...excessive heat of a brick chimney set fire to the floor* but that the *city engines* stopped the fire from spreading.**13**

Part of the drama of the final fire in 1895 was captured in a letter to the Chester Watch Committee:

On the morning of 30th May last as you are, doubtless aware we received an alarm of Fire the Brigade turned out when they found out it was the Dee Flour Mills, I at once returned to the Engine House for the Steam Fire Engine and other appliances and asked some firemen who was there to bring the Small Fire Escape down for fear it may be wanted, when they declined to do so, some time after I got the Steamer down, and at work; I heard the crashing of Slates, and looking round I saw 3 men on a low part of the roof, and at once saw the danger as one man was part way through, I then said there are too many men on that roof one man had better come off when one fireman named Moore turned round and used most disgraceful language to me asking me what the H..l it had to do with me, mind your own b....y business, go to the b....y Engine, that is your place....someone then spoke to him about his conduct...he then said...he is only a Corporation Servant and nothing to do with us.....

Looking back over a period of more than 800 years, the mills have experienced many threats and changes. However, it is remarkable that, although the mills' superstructures have gone, the ancient infrastructure of both the weir and water-channels have survived to the end of the 20th century.

References

1. W. Aryton, 'Records relating to the River Dee and its Fisheries' 'Journal of the Chester Archaeological Society', 6, 1849-55, pp., 245-246.
2. R. Stevenson and Sons, 'Report to George Johnson, agent for the Marquis of Westminster', 5 March, 1840, p. 2.
3. The Chester Hydro-electric plant, 'Electrical Review', 73, (1873), 17 October 1913, p. 619.
4. F. Simpson, 'The River Dee' in 'Journal of Chester Archaeological Society', 14, 1908, p. 105.
5. H. Roberts, 'Chester Guide' (Chester: First Published 1851, this edition - Chester City Archives, 1996), p. 56.

6. Harleian MSS. 2083.600b., Bennett, 'Some Feudal Mills', p. 97.
7. "The Causeway Mills in Handbridge", In 'The Cheshire Sheaf', January, 1954, p. 3.
8. Chester City Record Office (C.R.O), ML/2/307.
9. J. Hemingway, 'History of the City of Chester', vol. ii, p. 434.
10. CRO, Chester Assembly Book, A/F/30 (14 Aug. 1649), p. 21.
11. Bennett, 'Feudal Mills', p. 123.
12. C.R O, 'Fire at water corn mills' in 'Cuttings', 072714 (1819).
13. ibid, 'Fire at Snuff mills' (1701).
14 C.R.O. Watch Committee Minutes CCB 20, 345/6

Old Maps and Pictures

Braun's map of Chester, published between 1572 and 1618, shows the Handbridge Fulling Mills as two buildings with double ridged roofs separated by a mill race. Speed's map of 1610 names the *Fulling Mills* in Handbridge and shows them as three adjacent single ridged buildings, in line on the river bank (both not illustrated).

The mid-17th century drawing by Randle Holmes, taking into account 'artistic licence', provides much information about the mills and waterworks. On the city side of the river was Tyrer's Water Tower, incorrectly drawn as a square tower centrally over the Bridgegate, rather than an octagonal on the west tower. Also, shown on the city side are two single-storey buildings. These were raised on a plinth above the river. Both buildings had ridged roofs, whose eaves were about level with the parapet of the Dee Bridge. Within these buildings were three waterwheels. On the downstream side were three mill races. A weir is shown diagonally across the river. On the Handbridge side there was a single-storey, ridged roof building on an island, with a waterwheel on its south wall (This mill was called The Mill by Itself). Portrayals of a salmon cage and weir are shown below the Handbridge Mill and sited on its tailrace. The small stone island in the King's Pool, known locally as Swan or Duck Island, which still exists, is also shown. The other two mills on the Handbridge bank are not shown.

Dee Mills, c1640   *By Randle Holmes, from the Harleian MSS*

De Lavaux's 1745 map shows the *Water Cause Way* (weir): *The Bridge Tower* (Tyrer's Water Tower) and the *Dee Mills* and *Water Engine* on the city end of the Dee Bridge. Between the castle and the river were the *The Skinners Houses*, which housed the workshops of animal skinners. The *Skinner's Hall* was in *Clayton Lane* (now Duke Street), near to the later Wishing Steps.

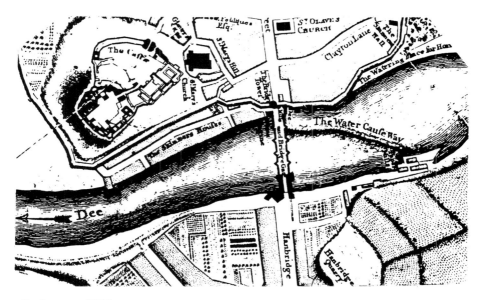

De Lavaux, 1745

On the *Hanbridge* side are three mills, two on the river bank (the Upper and Lower Fulling Mills) and one on the island (the Mill by Itself), separated from the river bank by a mill race. De Lavaux shows the Handbridge mills as *Paper Mills*, but a conveyance of 1698 refers only to the *Lower Fulling Mill* as converted to a paper mill, while the *Higher Fulling Mill* was in the possession of the Clothworkers' and Walkers' company. The use of the *Mill by It Self* was not stated.1 However, in 1806 the tradition was that:

*From time immemorial factories and similar works have been established on the southern banks of the Dee between the causeway and the Old Bridge - tanning, skinning and barking, being all carried on there... some indeed to our present day.*2

In 1848, Tithe Maps show that the Handbridge mills were engaged in processing animal skins, while trade directories show that work connected with animal by-products continued there into the late 19th century. Although a 1745 map by De Lavaux only names paper mills in Handbridge, fulling and/or skin processing was almost certainly carried out there. No changes appear to have occurred in the period between De Lavaux's 1745 map and Burdett's 1777 map (not illustrated).

Old Dee Bridge and Snuff Mills, 1819   George Cuitt Junior   Courtesy of the Grosvenor Museum

Up until the late 18th century, the Chester mills were illustrated as relatively small buildings attached to large undershot wheels. Millers did not become responsible for the storage of grain until the end of the 16th century. As a result, and with an expansion of trade in the 18th century, grain mills were to need far more space. The upper granary floor with its large storage provision and hoist was a product of this expansion.3

Wenham remarks in 'Watermills', that mills were true vernacular buildings in that, almost from the start, they were built in the local styles and materials easily available in the locality. Originally, the mills may have been constructed of wattle and daub with a thatched roof but, as their value grew and was recognised, later examples were built in stone, brick or half-timber, depending on the local tradition. This tradition continued, with very few exceptions, until the 18th century. It was not until the 18th and 19th centuries that the grander mills made their appearance.4

An 1819 illustration of the 'Old Dee Bridge and Snuff Mills', by George Cuitt junior, enables a direct comparison to be made between the style of early and later mills. In the foreground is the much older and truly vernacular Mill Behind the Snuff Mill or The Higher Fulling Mill. The overall appearance of this small mill was ramshackle, with a turf or thatched roof and walls constructed from rough boarding. The undershot wheel and sluice are clearly visible. It may not be unreasonable to assume that all the early Handbridge mills were of similar construction to the Higher Fulling Mill. The much larger brick building, behind the Higher Fulling Mill, is the late 18th or early 19th century Snuff Mill.

Part of `A South Prospect of the City of Chester`, 1749   *J Boydell*
Courtesy of the Grosvenor Museum

J. Boydell's painting 'A South Prospect of the City of Chester' published in 1749, shows a view of the Water Tower, Water Works and the Dee Mills from downstream of the Dee Bridge. The main mill building was constructed on a plinth above the river and was three storeys high. The ground floor had a tall loading door onto the river, with a greater floor to ceiling height than the 1st and 2nd floors. The mill had a flat roof. A much smaller building with a pitched roof, and two water-wheels on either side, was sited on the downstream side of the main mill building. To the left of the mill buildings were the Water Works and Water Tower. The water-wheel between the mill and the Water Works probably drove the water-engine. At the base of the Water Works at river level can be seen, what may be, water intakes. Along the river bank were the workshops of the animal skinners.

In addition to Boydell's 1749 painting, Moses Griffith's (1747-1819) pre-1781 upstream view of the mills (not illustrated) provides a comprehensive picture of how the north bank of the River Dee appeared in the middle to late 18th century.

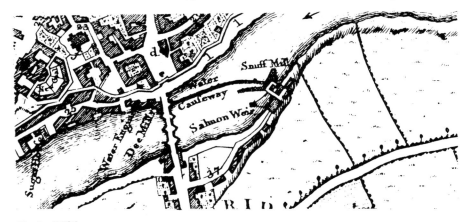

Poole, 1791

Poole's 1791 map shows substantial structural changes to the Handbridge mills, now called the *Snuff Mills*. The island site had been developed and a 'link' made with the mills on the river bank. Also, structures appear along the north face of the old Handbridge Quarry face and adjacent to the south end of the Dee Bridge. The Salmon Cage and Weir are shown, but only the *Salmon Weir* is named. The *Water Engine* and *Dee Mills* were still present at the north end of the Dee Bridge, but the Water Tower had been removed in 1781.

Ormerod's 1817 plan of Chester shows further structural changes to the Handbridge mills, which were still called the *Snuff Mills*. The Salmon Cage is shown, but not named. There appears little change to the properties along the north face of Handbridge quarry. The *Dee Mill* and *Water Engine* were shown at the city end of the Old Dee Bridge. *Skinners Lane* lies between *The Castle* and the river.

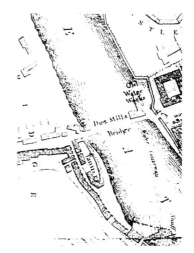

Ormerod, 1817   **Wood, 1833**

In the early 1830s the county authorities acquired the industrial area around Skinner's Lane, which housed the workshops of the animal skinners, and extended the city wall to enclose it, as shown on Wood's 1833 map. The leather workers had moved to the old Handbridge Quarry site, near to the Handbridge mills. A *Tannery* is shown at the south end of the bridge. The Handbridge mills had even more structural changes in the 1817 to 1833 period. *The Dee Mills* and *Old Water Works* are shown at the city end of the Dee *Bridge*.

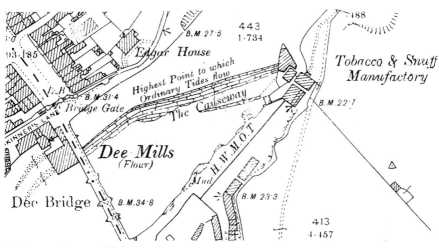

Ordnance Survey, 1900

41

The OS map of 1900 shows the *Dee Mills (Flour)* with two tail races at the city end of the bridge. The Water Works is shown but not named. *Skinner's Lane* was still present, but in the first few years of the 20th century the muddle of buildings in this area was removed. The Handbridge mills were called the *Tobacco & Snuff Manufactory*, with even further structural changes in the period 1833 to 1900. There was a *Skin Yard* near to the southern end of the bridge and domestic dwellings were crammed between the west face of the old quarry and behind the properties fronting Handbridge thoroughfare. Early in the 20th century, the settlement was declared unhealthy, and the Council obtained an order to demolish these properties.

By the late 18th/early 19th century, Chester's small, vernacular mill buildings had been replaced by much grander industrial structures. At the city end of the bridge, ever more mill space was needed to match the growth in population and its associated demand for flour. In Handbridge, extra space was required to meet the growth of the snuff and tobacco industry. These industries needed increased space, with reasonable natural lighting, arranged in such a way that power could easily be distributed throughout the buildings. The outcome was a form of building, similar to the early silk mills, taking the traditional constructional techniques of brick and stone load-bearing walls and timber beam-and-plank floors as its basis. The preferred factory shape of long and thin in plan could not be attained at Chester because of the restricted sites. However, additional space was made available by building several storeys upwards and by replacing small sundry structures by much larger, space-efficient ones.

The Dee Mills, 1852   *Artist Unknown, Courtesy of The Grosvenor Museum*

The mills at the city end of the bridge were burnt down in 1789, but in 1790 permission was granted to rebuild and extend them. Several 19th century illustrations show the rebuilt mills towering over the bridge by several storeys. The Dee Mill was a typical industrial building of the period, with a regular rectangular plan, shallow pitched roof and uniform windows. A ship is moored by the central loading bays on the south end of the mill. Above the loading bays, at roof level, can be seen a sack hoist, which was powered by a water-wheel. The sack hoist transported grain to the top of the mill where it was put in the grain bin.

At the turn of the 19th century Frank Simpson, a Chester local historian, took many photographs of Chester. His photographs show the Dee Mills at the north end of the bridge after the disastrous fire of 1895. The view from Edgar's Field in Handbridge shows that the mill had changed little from earlier 19th century paintings. On the downstream side of the mill were odd little canopied structures over the mill tail races. On the south end of the mill were bays for loading or unloading ships. The 1895 fire destroyed the central portion of the mill, which was never rebuilt. The view from the city reveals the various floor levels of the mill. Since earlier paintings, a tall central chimney had appeared, which may have served a central boiler house to provide steam to power a steam engine. In front of the chimney and mill was the Old Water Works building.

The Dee Mills From The City, Late 1890s   *Frank Simpson*
Courtesy of The Grosvenor Museum

43

In 1913, an hydro-electric power station was opened on the site of the Dee Mills (flour). In 1996, with the exception of few modifications, the exterior of the building remains much as built in 1913.

In 1899, a rather complicated arrangement of irregular shaped buildings existed at the Handbridge end of the weir. They were three storey high, industrial buildings, which were linked over the mill race. These were demolished early in the 20th century and replaced by the impressive Thomas Nicholls and Co. Tobacco Factory, built on the side of the river bank, with the island site remaining undeveloped. This factory was demolished in the 1960s.

Nicholls' factory was replaced by *Salmon Leap* residential flats, in true 60's architectural concrete style. In the early 1970s, a migratory fish counter was built on the island site, above the 'salmon steps'.

These maps, prints and photographs suggest that the early Chester mills were relatively small vernacular buildings. The largest was the three-storey flour mill at the city end of the bridge. The maps show, at the Handbridge end of the weir, three single-storey buildings which were used as fulling and paper mills. Oddly, although a bark mill almost certainly existed, none of the maps recorded this fact. Maps also record a Water Engine/Water Works and Water Tower at the city end of the bridge, and a salmon weir and cage in Handbridge.

By the late 18th/early 19th century, the old buildings were replaced by much larger, multi-storey brick structures. These were typical industrial structures of the period. Larger mills were needed to meet the increasing demand for flour by an expanding population, and to cater for the growing addiction to snuff and tobacco.

Early in the 20th century, an impressive building for the manufacture of tobacco was built in Handbridge, which survived until the mid-20th century. A block of flats and a migratory fish counting station now occupy the site of the Handbridge mills.

Although most of the physical evidence of the mills has disappeared, thankfully, the weir and associated water channels are intact to provide archaeological evidence of Chester's water power system.

References

1. 'The Causeway Mills In Handbridge', 'Cheshire Sheaf', Volume XLIX,
    January 1954, p. 3.
2   ibid., p. 4.
3. Wenham, 'Watermills', p. 28.
4. ibid., p. 28.

The Dee Mills Viewed From Across the King's Pool, Late 1890s   Unknown (possibly Frank Simpson)   *Courtesy of Chester Record Office*

Water Power

It is known that the Romans used water power in Britain: three water mill sites have been excavated along Hadrian's Wall. Known generally as Vitruvian mills, after Vitruvius the engineer who first described them, they were probably like the waterwheels used extensively in Britain from the 8th century onwards, which had horizontal shafts with flat buckets that dipped into fast-flowing rivers or streams.

Little is known of the development of water power during the Dark Ages, but by the Domesday Survey, begun in 1080 and completed in 1086, there were over 5,000 corn mills in England, most of them south and east of the rivers Trent and Severn.1 There was a wide spread tendency, at the time of the survey and indeed much later, to refer to individual pairs of millstones as mills. It is reasonable to assume that most of the mills recorded must have originated in Saxon times, because they could not have all sprung up when the Normans gained control. The majority of these mills employed 'undershot' water wheels.

The Domesday Survey at Chester did not record any mills but, in 1093, a corn mill was authorised at the Dee Bridge, Chester. Hugh Lupus, Earl of Chester, granted the site to the Abbey of St. Werburgh. The Harleian MSS records that:

The River Dee was drawne into the saide cittie with great change by the earle [Lupus], or some of his predecessors, before the conqueste, from the ancient course which it held before, a myle or two distant from the cittie, and a passage for it cutt out of a rock under the walls of the said cittie; and the said earle also built the corn mills of Chester and erected the causey [weir]. 2

This statement causes some confusion as it would seem a physical impossibility that the Dee's course was ever a mile or two away from the city. However, if the phrase *a mile or two* is seen as a hyperbole or colloquialism rather than a statement of fact, then the statement starts to make some sense. Prior to the construction of the weir, the level of the Dee upstream from Chester was several feet lower than today, except at high tides. The increased river level, caused by the weir, would certainly bring it much closer to the city walls than previously, when it may have run on the Handbridge side of, or over, the Earl's Eye (island), now known as The Meadows. Also, the bedrock of the river is soft Bunter sandstone, which could easily have been quarried or cut through.

One explanation is that the river may have been 'canalised' from Heronbridge to form the 'straight mile' thus increasing the 'head' and velocity of the River Dee. This, in conjunction with the weir which drove water into a narrow channel would increase the available potential energy of the river to drive the waterwheels. It would also provide the valuable addition of wet meadow-land for cattle grazing, a navigable river to Heronbridge and a better defence for the city.

View Of Handbridge Mills From The City*, 1892*
From `Illustrated Chester`.

Unknown Photographer
Digitised by Steve Howe

The technology of water power was well established and understood at the time of Hugh Lupus. As stated, in order to obtain a head of water for milling and facilitate fish traps, a stone weir or causeway was constructed across the Dee. The requirements of a waterwheel are a head of water to drive it, a consistent and controllable flow of water and avoidance, if possible, of flooding. On a large flowing river, with a relatively low gradient, the easiest and cheapest mill to build would have a short leat taking water to the wheel which, because only a low head is available, would have to be of the undershot type. At that time most mills had undershot wheels.

The Dee Mills were susceptible to flooding and a more reliable siting involved longer leats and tailraces (to avoid water backing up on the wheel) with a low weir in the river. By using a longer leat a greater head of water was made available. The River Dee is particularly susceptible to changes in level, but a long weir placed diagonally across the stream minimised these effects. The longest weir possible combined the merits of long leats in creating a consistent head of water at all times and an efficient governor for the wheels, with the least variation in water level during spates.

The Dee Mills (grain), at the city end of the bridge was fed by a headrace via two arches of the bridge. The water ran under the mill and drove at least two undershot waterwheels, then discharged into two tailraces. The later water engine, at the water works, supplied water for Chester. The simple undershot wheel was cheap and easy to install, needed a minimum of groundworks to arrange its water supply and did the job for which it was required effectively if not efficiently. Mechanical efficiency was of little importance because there was adequate water in the Dee all year round to drive low powered wheels reliably. The water engine was a different matter! It was a sophisticated device: consisting of an undershot waterwheel which drove a series of pumps, that forced water through pipes to a cistern high on the top of Tyrer's tower.

At the Handbridge end of the weir, a channel was cut for a millrace, thus forming an artificial island. A 1911 plan shows that four mills once existed at the Handbridge end of the weir during some part of the 19th century. One, or two parallel water-wheels powered mills M1 and M3, whilst mills M2 and M4 were powered by separate water-wheels. By 1895, only the waterwheel that powered M1 mill survived.

In 1989, after a year-long restoration project, the Handbridge wheel was officially reopened. (see rear cover photograph). In 1987, Cyril T G Boucher, Millwright and Chartered Engineer, had reported on the surviving waterwheel:

The present wheel is an undershot one of composite construction, and carries on the same axle a large spur wheel which once drove, by means of a pinion on a lay shaft, the machinery to the mill. By historical standards the wheel is comparatively modern and dates from about 1860-70.

...there are clear indications of a much earlier set up, for the mill race which has been artificially divided into two, once had a wheel of the same diameter but a breath of 8' or so...[3]

Alternatively, there may have been two parallel wheels, similar to the Morden Snuff Mill arrangement, which independently drove M1 and M3 mills.

On one side of the rim of the Handbridge wheel is an iron toothed ring, which was a later improvement to waterwheels, and enabled the power to be taken off directly, without the necessity for transmission through a gudgeon (pivot at the end of axle on which the wheel turns)

The first waterwheels were constructed of wood. There were three main types of waterwheel: wooden wheels, metal wheels and the hybrids (composite) made from both. Wooden wheels were mounted on axletrees that were seldom less than 45cm square in section. Two pairs of spokes made up each side of the wheel. Set at right angles to each other they clasped the axle in the space created by their intersection - hence they were called clasp-arm wheels. A wheel did not fit exactly around its axle. The final position of the wheel in relation to its hub was determined by the stout wedges that were driven in at each face of the axle. At the ends of the parallel spokes the felloes (rim sections of wheels assembled from parts) were fixed and this gave the wheel recognisable form.

Eight segments were common around the rim and each joint was strengthened by the addition of an iron band bolted to each side of the felloe. The stout pegs that supported the paddle boards were mortised through the rim and fixed into place with pins or bolts. Very early wheels of this kind would probably have been held together with wooden pins.[4]

The development of cast iron in the 18th century allowed many improvements to be made in machines of all kinds, and provided many advantages to the millwright, when used in conjunction with timber. Clasp-arm wheels were not particularly strong at their centres where the spokes were wedged on to the axletree. A casting, however, could solve the problem and supply a truer and stronger centre. Stronger and more accurate rims could be made in cast iron and this helped to produce a wheel with a better balance. Even working wheels of wood reached a stage when they had to be replaced. The introduction of a new wheel made entirely of metal could be very expensive for the miller, as alterations would have to be made to internal machinery. The most economic way of providing a new wheel which had some of the advantages of the metal ones as to construct a wheel on the old - and usually heavy - wooden axle.[5]

Between 1750 and 1850 the waterwheel came into its own for industrial purposes, well after the steam engine had become firmly established. Water had been the primary source of power in the early years of the Industrial Revolution and the steam engine was at first as much a product of industrial growth as a contributor to its development. Waterwheels were cheap and easy to install and could drive machinery which the early non-rotative steam engine could not. Indeed, in the mid-18th century steam engines were used to pump back the tail water of the water-wheel and even supply water to wheels that had no streams of their own.6

In coastal areas tide mills took advantage of the fact that water could be ponded up in a small estuary or creek at high tide and used to drive a water-wheel. However for river mills, such as those on the Dee at Chester, this was a great disadvantage to the millers. The incoming tide would backup onto the tail race of the water-wheels, eventually stopping them completely. The millers were forced to work in between tides, sometimes into the night and early morning.

In summary, the evidence presently available suggests that as many as six undershot water-wheels powered the mills on both sides of the River Dee. In 1989, a composite waterwheel was restored at the site of the old Handbridge Snuff Mills.

References

1. N.Cossons, 'The BP book of Industrial Archaeology' (London: David & Charles, 1987), p. 46.
2. Harleian MSS., 2084. 157. cited in R.Bennett, 'Some Feudal Mills', p. 57.
3. C.T.G. Boucher, Report on "The Snuff Mill Wheel, Chester' (1987) at the Certificate of Commendation at the 1900th Anniversary of the City of Chester for the restoration of Stretton watermill.
4. J.Vine, 'Discovering Watermills' (Shire Publications, 1993 - 6th Edition), p.7
5. ibid., p. 8.
6. Cossons, 'The BP book of Industrial Archaeology', p. 48.

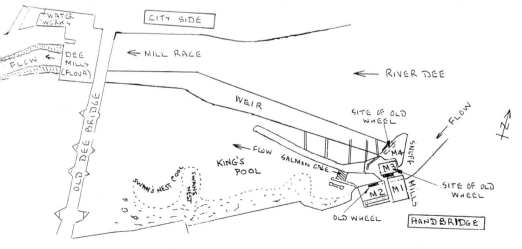

The Chester Weir and Mills, Based on a 1911 Plan   *Roy Wilding*

Handbridge Mill, Link Over Mill Race, Late 1890s

Corn Mills

The waterwheel generated the motion that was carried into the interior of the mill by the great axle. At the end of the axle was placed the pit wheel. Half of this component was permanently within the narrow pit that gave it its common name. In ancient mills the pit wheel was usually constructed from timber. At a later stage of development the wooden wheels were replaced by iron ones. Iron wheels, however, frequently had wooden teeth and which almost always occurred when the replacement of a pit wheel did not coincide with the replacement of the original wooden shaft.[1]

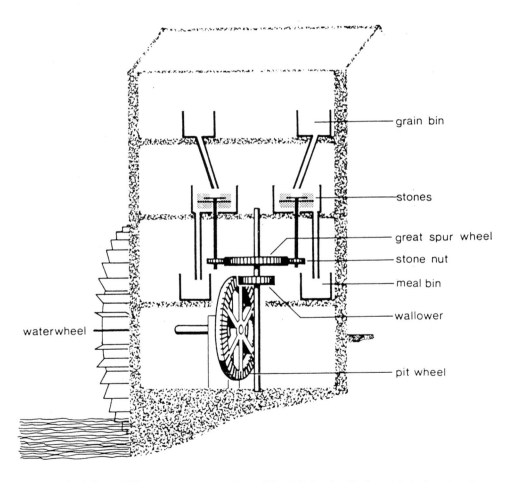

grain bin

stones

great spur wheel

stone nut

meal bin

wallower

waterwheel

pit wheel

A Typical Corn Mill
Courtesy : David & Charles

From 'The B P Book of Industrial Archaeology'

The music of the mill is described by Thomas Hardy in his contemporary account of a 19th century corn mill in the novel 'The Trumpet-Major':

*She lived with her widowed mother in a portion of an ancient building formerly a manor-house, but now a mill, which, being too large for his own requirements, the miller had found it convenient to divide and appropriate in part to these highly respectable tenants. In this dwelling Mrs Garland's and Anne's ears were soothed morning, noon, and night by the music of the mill, the wheels and cogs of which, being of wood, produced notes that might have borne in their minds a remote resemblance to the wooden tones of the stopped diapason (one of the two principal foundation stops in an organ) in an organ. Occasionally, when the miller was bolting (sifting flour), there was added to these continuous sounds the cheerful clicking of the hopper, which did not deprive them of rest except when it was kept going all night; and over and above all this they had the pleasure of knowing that there crept in through every crevice, door, and window of their dwelling, however tightly closed, a subtle mist of superfine flour from the grinding-room, quite invisible, but making its presence known in the course of time by giving a pallid and ghostly look to the best furniture...*2

To convert the horizontal line of the axle into the vertical plane the pit wheel meshed into a smaller wallower wheel. This latter wheel, frequently of iron, caused the heavy shaft to rotate; and as it had fewer teeth than the pit wheel the speed of the shaft was increased by a ratio of about four or more to one.

Mounted just above the wallower was the spur wheel which carried the motion to the millstones via the stone nut. The spur wheel, which rotated at about four times faster than the axle, was larger and had more teeth than the wallower. When it drove the relatively small stone nut the ratio was increased by seven or eight to one. A stone nut therefore revolved many times faster than the waterwheel - about 28 to 1.3

The Dee Mills were exceptionally large compared with 'typical' rural flour mills. They operated on a very large-scale and were housed in extensive, multi-storey structures. As early as 1291, the names of individual Chester corn mills were recorded as *Cobquell,* which derived from `cwellan` to quell or kill and `cobbe`, a seeding head of corn.4 In 1608, there existed *...five corn mills and one malt mill under two several roofs...*5 In 1807, there were ... *12 pair of stones, six of which are French...*6

Many mills operated two types of stone, Derbyshire Peak and French burr stones. Derbyshire Peak stones of grey millstone grit were used for barley, but flour was usually processed on the harder French burr stones which were more suitable for finer grinding. These latter stones were not cut from a single piece, as were the Derbyshire ones, but built up out of sections of quartz cemented together and bound with iron bands. The surfaces of the stones had a series of radial grooves in them which facilitated the grinding of the grain and encouraged the resultant meal outwards towards the rim. The stones would be dressed or resharpened from time to time.7

The Dee Mills were not only ideally located just at the edge of the city and well inland, but were also accessible by sea-going vessels. The operation of all water-powered corn mills, including the Dee Mills, was similar and very simple. A lucam (a projecting dormer cabin, usually made of wood) projected from its upper floor and contained hoisting-gear. A sack-hoist lifted sacks of grain from carts or ships (in the case of the Dee Mills) from under the lucam. The grain was stored in bins on the top floor - the 'bin' or 'granary' floor. When required for grinding, the grain was released from the bin and flowed down chutes by gravity to a lower floor called the 'stone' floor. The grain entered the 'hopper' and was fed into the centre or eye of the top stone of the two which comprised the 'grinding-tool'. The top stone was called the 'runner stone', and was turned by the power supplied through wheels and gears from the main waterwheel. The bottom or 'bed stone' was fixed, and the grain was nipped in the gaps between the stones, broken down into flour and worked its way to the edge. The height of the runner stone above the bed stone was controlled by the miller, and it governed the degree of fineness of the flour produced. The process was assisted by the pattern - hardy changed since it was developed by the Romans - etched into the surface of the stones. The grain was effectively cut in a scissor-like motion as the runner stone revolved with the flour working its way by centrifugal force along channels in the surface of the bed stone. The stones and flour were enclosed in a wooden box called a 'tun'. From the tun the flour fell to the ground floor, where it was bagged up for transporting away from the mill or taken back to a higher floor for further processing.**8**

References

1. J. Vince , 'Discovering Watermills' (Princes Risborough: Shire, 1993), p.16.
2. T. Hardy, 'The Trumpet-Major' (Oxford University Press, 1991 ed), p.8.
3. Vince, 'Discovering Watermills', p. 16.
4. J. McN Dodgson, 'The Place-Names of Cheshire', Part Five (Section 1:i), English Place Name Society (Cambridge: English University Press, 1981), p.52.
5. Harl. MSS. 2081.216. cited in R. Bennett, 'Some Feudal Mills', p. 100.
6. R. Bennett, 'Some Feudal Mills', p. 123.
7. N. Cussons, 'The BP book of Industrial Archaeology', p. 43.
8. P. Wenham, 'Watermills' (London: Hale, 1989), p. 38.

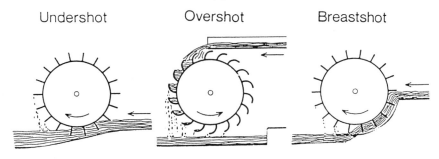

Undershot   Overshot   Breastshot

Types of Waterwheels

Fulling Mills

In 1355, reference was made to *mylnes of Dee on both parts of Dee, as well as the walker* (fulling) *mylnes...* and in 1394, *a certain place of land upon which stand the `tentoria`* (drying frames) *of our lord the king belonging to his fulling mills of Dee.*1 The weaving trade in Chester was both important and organised by 1399, when many master weavers took part in an affray against the journeymen opposite St Peter's Church on the feast of Corpus Christi. Stewards of the Weavers' Company were named in the Pentice Court roll in 1438-39 and by the middle of the 15th century, it was apparently associated with the fullers and the chaloners. The fullers were based in the fulling mills on the Handbridge side of the Dee, and carried out part of the cloth finishing process. The chaloners were blanket makers. The weavers and walkers (or fullers) appear together in a list of companies in 1475-76 and in the Chester cycle of Mystery Plays produced the last play, 'the Last Judgement'. In the 15th century, the journeymen weavers had their own company, but it had disappeared long before the weavers received their charter from the Mayor and Citizens in 1583. For most of the 18th century, the company met in a building in St John's Churchyard, not too far from the river and the mills, probably the Hermitage, used earlier by the Shoemakers' Company. By the end of the century, however, the company held its meeting in the local inns, for example the 'Boot' in Eastgate Street, the 'Pied Bull' in Northgate Street and the 'Blossoms' in Foregate Street. By 1835, the company had only 10 members.2

Fulling: A Carving From A
Roman Grave Stone

From `The Woollen Industry`
by Chris Aspin
Shire Album 81

Water was employed to drive a wide variety of industrial equipment, beginning with the water-powered textile fulling mill that was probably developed during the 12th century. Fulling, the thickening and cleaning of newly woven cloth, was an ancient craft that was carried out in Roman times. The fuller stood in a tub of warm water, as illustrated by the carving on a Roman gravestone, and trampled underfoot cloth covered with a detergent such as fullers' earth. Friction caused the wet woollen fibres to mat together, or felt, reducing the size of a piece of cloth by as much as a third.3

The 'walking' of cloth continued in remote parts of the British Isles until the early 20th century.4

In the past, fulling mills were described as 'walker`, `walk`, or `walking` mills' for, as already seen, the earliest form of fulling was to walk on the cloth, possibly with the cloth placed in a stream or river. Fulling mills may also have been known as 'walking mills' because if the water power was insufficient at any time, during dry weather or times of frost, then men would tread or *walk the wheel* to provide power.5 Fulling was the first woollen process to be mechanised and, as such, represented the first stage in the transition of woollen manufacturing from a domestic craft to a factory industry. It was only in the second half of the 20th century that the use of hammers for fulling became obsolete. Fulling machines were called 'stocks', which were used by placing cloth in the 'box' of the machine against the curved wooden breast and pounding it with considerable force with a pair of hammers which were lifted and released alternatively by wooden tappet wheels. The 'feet' of the hammers were shaped so that the cloth was constantly turned. When the machine stopped, the hammers were held in the 'up' position by the 'stangs' which were thrust into slots in the feet.

In the fulling process, cloth was fulled three times under the hammers of the mill. The first time, urine was used and it was customary for carts to make regular rounds, collecting urine in casks which was sold to the fullers. The second fulling was with fuller's earth and this was followed by soap, placed in water:
*Made as hot as the hand could well bear it. The solution is to be poured by little and little upon the cloth to be fulled for at least two hours.*6

Finally, all traces of fulling materials were washed away by allowing a constant supply of clean water to fall into the stocks. In rural factories, fulled fabrics were hung in the open air for drying on tenter frames, which formed an essential part of the wool process. The tenter frame had horizontal and vertical bars studded with tenter hooks to which the lengths of cloth were stretched for drying in the open air. The saying *on tenterhooks* now represents the emotional condition of being stretched.

The Handbridge Fulling Mills may have employed an unusual method of cloth drying. The causeway on the Handbridge side of the river, below the weir was called the *Training Wall*. This wall still extends into the the river from the *island* and forms a barrier between the *Salmon Steps* and the mill-race.7 The fulled cloth may have been *trained along this wall to dry.*

By 1698, the Handbridge *Lower Fulling Mill* had been converted to a paper mill, although the *Higher Fulling Mill* was still in the possession of the Clothworkers' company.8 Fulling probably ceased in Handbridge sometime in the 18th century, and was replaced by snuff, needle and paper-making mills.

Fulling Cloth at the Pantarddulais Pandy   *Courtesy: Museum of Welsh Life*

References

1.   J. McN. Dodgson, `The Place-Names of Cheshire`, pp.47-49.
2.   Chester City Record Publication, 'Guildhall', (Chester: 1992), p. 17.
3.   Kilburn-Scott, 'Early Cloth Fulling and Its Machinery', 'Transactions of the Newcomen Society', XII, 1931-2, p. 1.
4.   C. Aspin, 'The Woollen Industry', (Princes Risborough: Shire, 1994), p. 25.
5.   J.G. Rollins, 'Needle Mills' (London: S.P.A.B., 1970), Fig. 6(a).
6.   A. Rees, 'Cyclopaedia', Vol. 15. p. 132.
7.   Environment Agency (Asian Yr Amgylchedd), Buckley, Unclassified papers relating to the Handbridge mills, 'Plan of the Handbridge Mills 1926/27'.
8.   'The Causeway Mills in Handbridge', 'Cheshire Sheaf', Vol. XLIX, January, 1954, p. 3.

Bark Mills

The Chester Leather Industry

The leather industry was important in medieval and post-medieval Chester for several reasons. The city was a port and an important trade centre, and was in close proximity to cattle and sheep raising communities. Also, water power was readily available to drive bark mills. Leather was used for shoes, clothes, horse equipment, bottles, bags, belts and straps. Chester had more of its population involved in the leather trade than elsewhere. In the late 16th and 17th century, 20% of all craftsmen in the city were leather workers. There were several distinct trades, from the preparation of leather to its conversion to finished goods. Processing involved the skinning and tanning of heavy hides such as that of cattle or horses by soaking in pits for up to 3 years, and also treating light skins such as sheep, deer, goat and game. Conversion of the raw leather to finished goods was carried out by trades such as curriers and glovers.1

Records from the early 16th century onward show, apart from local sales, that shoemakers sent their produce to Northwest England, saddlers to the Cheshire countryside and Ireland, glovers to London and Ireland, whilst in the 16th and 17th centuries tanned calf skins were exported to continental countries such as Spain and France.2

Chester Guilds

One of the earliest guilds to emerge were the tanners, who were first mentioned in 1361. In the list of companies in a mayor's book for 1475-76 they appear under the alternative name of barkers, because they used oak bark in the tanning process at the Handbridge mill. Many guilds were associated with the leather trade, including the Skinners, Glovers, Saddlers and Cordwainers.3

The Skinners' and Feltmakers' Guild existed in 1433. In that year, the mayor and sheriffs of Chester were ordered to find and punish all *foreigners* who used the trade of skinner and shoemaker within the liberties of Chester. Stewards of the Skinners' Company were named in the Pentice Court roll for 1448-9 and the company is amongst those listed in a mayor's book for 1475-6. In 1483, Edward, Prince of Wales, ordered that no skinner or shoemaker was to practice that trade in Chester without licence of the company on pain of £10.4 In 1608, there were 36 masters in the company. In 1835, there were only two members of the company, but it had revived by 1863, when new rules and regulations were issued.5

Cordwainers or corvisers, and shoemakers, practiced similar trades, and their guild was called the Cordwainers' and Shoemakers' Company. As early as 1356, one of the Chester rows was known as 'le Corvyserrow'. The earliest surviving charter granted to

58

Impressionist View of The Mills and Skin Houses, Late C18th or Early C19th a Chester company was granted to the Shoemakers by Edward, the Black Prince, in 1370, reversing a decision made eight years earlier which forbade them to meddle in the tanners' trade. For a brief period in the 15th century, cordwainers and shoemakers were amalgamated with skinners.**6**

Saddlers were recorded in Chester from 1392-93. In 1472, the Saddlers' and Curriers' Company was given a monopoly by Edward IV to last 40 years. In 1639, the company was granted another charter, on this occasion by the city. The saddlers amalgamated with the curriers, who were leather dressers. During the 16th and 17th centuries, they fought to protect their craft against the shoemakers and the cutlers. Their dispute with the latter was over the sale of spurs.**7**

Chester Tanneries

The bark mill was located in Handbridge. The skinners' yard, tanneries, workshops and warehouses were mainly concentrated to the south of the city, on the opposite bank of the river, between the walls and the Dee. However, some tanning was also concentrated in the area to the north of Foregate Street. The collection of buildings between the old south wall of the city and the River Dee, between the castle and the Dee Mills, were referred to as the *Mustard houses,* the *glovers' houses* and *the skinners houses* and *lane.* In 1392-3, mustard-makers are mentioned at Chester. Robert Mustard lived here and gave his name to the property. It is likely that a mustard-maker would take the name Mustard. The city glovers and skinners took on the lease of the property but no dates can be found. In 1547, reference was made to *Muck Hill* in this area, which was a common midden.**8** From the 1830s, the leather workers moved from the city side of the river to the old Handbridge Quarry site, near to the bark mill. The 1848 Tithe Map shows a bark mill, skinners' yard and associated buildings in Handbridge. However, by the early 20th century the leather industry had disappeared from Handbridge.

Until the end of the 19th century, oak-bark tanneries were as commonplace in Britain as the saddlery and boot-making trades that they served. Hides from local farms, butchers, slaughter-houses and abroad were converted into leather by a long immersion in a mixture of oak bark and water.**9**

The main raw material used in the old tanneries were cattle hides that were processed in a series of tan pits to produce leather designed for boot soles and uppers, and horse saddles, collars and harness. In addition, the leather, if it was to be used for horse harness of boot uppers, had to be passed from the tanner to another leather worker - the currier or dresser, who prepared tanned leather for the saddlers and boot-makers by adding oils and grease to the surface and polishing it with steel, glass, cork, stone and mahogany polishers.**10**

While the tanner's craft was one that required considerable knowledge of chemical processes, that of the currier demanded a high degree of skill in the use of hand tools that were entirely different from those used by any other craftsman. The tanner could not complete his work without the assistance of the currier, for the tanned leather was stiff and badly coloured, and although after three rollings it may have been good enough for boot soles, it was certainly not suitable for boot uppers and harness.11

From the mid-19th century the crafts of tanning and currying were usually carried out on the same premises by highly skilled, though separate and specialised, craftsmen. In earlier times, the craft of tanning and the craft of currying were always independent and separate. These peculiarities of the leather trade in Britain were the results of legislative interference which deemed it illegal to carry on together the two trades of tanning and currying.12

Tanning

There were three basic ways of turning skin into leather: chamoising, tawing and vegetable tanning.13 The latter was by far the most common method of tanning in post-medieval times. In this process, animal pelts were preserved by employing the chemical process of tanning. Tannin is present in a wide range of vegetable matter, but the most common source was oak bark obtained, preferably, from 25 or 35 year old coppice oak. This was ground in a bark mill and mixed with cold water to produce the tanning liquor.14

The principal categories of skins which were used at a tannery were: hides, kips and skins. Hides were the skins of larger, fully grown animals such as bulls, cows, horses and buffaloes. They were mainly used for making heavy harness leather and sole leather. They could be further sub-divided into: a) slaughter, market or green hides, b) dried hides, c) dried salted hides and d) wet salted hides.

a) Slaughter, market or green hides came from abattoirs in Britain. Hides varied greatly in substance, size and texture. In earlier times they would come from local sources. The City Assembly Minutes for 1710 noted that:
    .....notwithstanding the Mayor's Proclamation requireing all country Butchers to bring their hides and skins with their meat to the Market some of the said Butchers have neglected to bring the same and others have brought them to the market onely for a colour refusing to sell them at any reasonable rate because they had contracted privately for sale thereof, for the whole season or otherwise with their country neighbours and therefore carry the same back every Markett day...15

b) Dried hides were imported mainly from Argentina and Uruguay. They were also known as 'flint hides' and since they were has hard as horn they had to be soaked in water for some hours and then rubbed and beaten before tanning. c) Dried salted hides were mainly imported from the West Indies, Brazil and South Africa. Before they could be tanned, all traces of salt had to be removed. d) Wet salted hides, mainly from Australia and the Baltic region, arrived at tanneries tightly packed in casks containing brine. Again, all traces of salt had to be removed from them before liming and tanning.16

Kips were the skins of the younger of the large animals, such as the skins of heifers, younger oxen and horses. The leather derived from the skins was usually thinner, more supple and better for such purposes as making boot and shoe upper leather. Again, they could be market kips, dried, salted or brine kips. Skins came from the smaller animals such as sheep, goats, pigs and seals. These were used for such things as boot uppers, gloves, upholstery, book bindings, seats of saddles and for all other purposes were soft leather was required.17

The first process in the long business of tanning was to cleanse each hide in a water-pit. All traces of salt had to be removed from the imported hides, while dry hides had to be made supple by frequent soaking and rubbing. In the case of market hides, it was vital that all traces of blood were removed, as the presence of blood in leather leaves a dark stain and poor grain.18

In some tanneries, it was customary to keep one or two large mastiff dogs, and it is said that as soon as market hides were delivered to a tannery, each one was pegged to the ground so that the dogs could bite off any fats or flesh that adhered to the skins. The mastiffs were useful to guard the premises and keep under control the vast number of rats that always infested tanneries. In addition, the dogs' excreta when mixed with hot water was essential for treating certain types of soft leather before tanning.

Mastiffs used to guard tanneries, eat flesh off hides, control vast numbers of rats, and provide ecreta used in the tanning process.
Courtesy: Museum Of Welsh Life

Occasionally market hides could not be used immediately and in order to prevent putrefaction they were salted and kept for a few days. The cleaning of hides was usually carried out in a water pit, supplied with a constant supply of clean water. The presence of an overflow pipe ensured a gentle movement of the water. Many tanners believed that the best way to clean market hides was to place them for some hours in a swiftly flowing stream or river. It is therefore very likely that the Chester tanners used the River Dee to clean their market hides. In addition to removing impurities, the water bath had the effect of swelling up the fibres of the hide, bringing them back to as near as possible to the condition in which they left the animals' backs. Hides were usually left in the water pits for a week or so, but since the water was seldom changed, it was:

> *full of putrefaction bacteria, the action of which assisted the softening...at a cost of serious loss of valuable hide substance.*[19]

When market hides were particularly dirty, they had to be removed from the water pit and scraped with a blunt two-handed draw knife.[20]

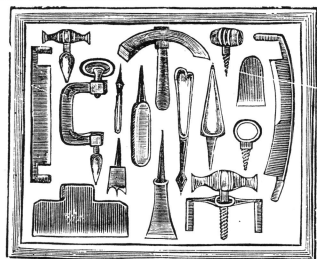

Tanning Tools
Bewick Woodcut

Unhairing and Fleshing

The craftsman responsible for the tasks of unhairing and fleshing was known as 'a beamsman', who worked in a building called a 'beam house'. The beam house, with its pits, wide doors and shutters, was specially designed for what must have been the most unhealthy and unpleasant tasks in the tannery. The beam, from which the workshop and craftsmen took their names, was a working table or horse with a convex or steeply sloping surface of iron or wood. The hide was thrown over this for unhairing and fleshing.[21]

Before the hides were taken to the beam house, however, they were placed in one of the three lime pits in order to loosen the epidermis and the fats and flesh that adhered to the corium or true skin. Slaked lime was mixed with water in various proportions and placed in the pits. The first pit in which the hides were soaked for a day or two contained a weak mixture of lime, very often a weak solution of old lime, highly charged with bacteria. The second pit contained a less mellow but slightly stronger mixture while the third contained a strong solution of new lime. The hides remained in the pits until the hair was easily removed, but the length of the liming depended partly on the quality of the leather required; the softer the leather, the longer the hide remained in the pit and the mellower the solution. For example, hides designed for sole leather had to be hard and tough and eight to ten days in strong lime was sufficient. Harness leather, on the other hand, which had to be more pliable, required mellow liming of 12 to 14 days, while soft shoe upper leather required anything up to six weeks in mellow lime. The skins were either suspended by chains from iron bars at the side of the pits or were allowed to float in the lime solution.**22**

Chester Assembly fire regulations for 1709 order that:

*no Tanner or other person within this City shall wilfully and voluntarily burn or set on fire any knaps or mudd taken out of any Tanpit or fat within the libertys of this city upon pain of Ten shillings for every such offence.***23**

With the tanner's hook, the hides were removed from the lime pits and placed over the beam, flesh side inwards. The beamsmen then took the blunt bladed, unhairing knife, curved to fit the convex surface of the beam. The hair was easily removed by pressing the knife downwards against the hides. It was important not only to remove the hair but also most of the hair root sheaths which could discolour the finished leather. The hair was not thrown away but was sold to plasterers and stone masons as an essential consituent of plaster and mortar. Some also went to upholsterers and manufacturers of cheap clothing.**24**

The fleshing operation was much more skilled than that of unhairing, for the flesh had to be removed in such a way as not to damage the true skin in any way. The slightest deviation of the knife could make a hide completely useless. The flesh was shaved away with a very sharp double-edged, two-handled knife. The concave edge was used for scraping, while the convex edge was used for cutting. Fleshings and other matters cut away at this stage were thrown into a pit. The fleshings were then taken away for making glue or gelatine.**25**

After unhairing and fleshing, pelts were thoroughly washed, and the heavier hides were again placed over the beam and the remaining lime squeezed out with a blunt knife called a 'scudder'. This usually had a slate blade. After a thorough washing and 'raising' in a weak acid solution, the heavy hides were ready for the tanning process itself. Lighter hides for making soft leather, such as those of calves, seals or sheep, were not washed after unhairing and fleshing, neither were they scudded.

The 'slitters', as they were called, were thrown into one of the pits at the back of the beamhouse. These were the 'mastering pits' and they contained a mixture of either hen or pigeon dung and cold water, a mixture known as 'bates'; or a mixture of warm water and dog excreta known as a 'pure' or 'drench'. The acid liquor of the mastering pits removed the lime, without any danger of damaging the pelt by scudding. Great care had to be taken not to leave the pelts in the mastering pit for too long as the solution would rapidly reduce the substance of the hides. In the case of bates, skins were immersed for a period of 10 to 12 days, but a few hours was sufficient in a drench. The slitters were again thoroughly washed in the water-pit (or river) before tanning.**26**

Rounding

Before a hide was tanned it had to be divided into several parts, a process known as 'rounding'. The reason for this was that a hide contains several qualities of skin, so that if a complete hide were immersed in the tanning liquor, the course-grained and open-pored offal would absorb the best tanning. The rounding table was an ordinary wooden trestle table, some 60 inches long and 30 inches wide. On this a hide was rounded with a sharp butcher's knife. The cheeks, the most inferior part of the hide, were first removed, then the shoulders or forepart, and the two sides of the bellies leaving the thickest and best part of the hide, known as the 'butt'. At the end of the tanning process, the butt could be divided into two sections known as 'bends' which could be used for the best quality sole and harness leather. Hides were again washed, occasionally in a weak solution of boracic acid and were then ready for the actual tanning.28

Leaching

To make tanning liquor, the craftsman needed a vast quantity of oak bark, ground finely and mixed with cold water in the so called 'leaching pits'. In the past oak was especially grown in coppices and the bark harvested after some 25 or 35 years' growth. The coppicing of oak trees was an extremely expensive process, and vast quantities of bark were required by every tannery. Some 18th century farmers regarded the production of oak bark as an essential part of their economy and the demand for good quality oak bark at that time was very large indeed. In more recent times, bark was obtained as a by-product of winter-felled oak trees or those felled during the spring months. It was far easier to remove the bark from spring-felled oak. The bark which may still be seen today at the Rhaeadr Tannery is from the Forest of Dean and the method of stripping there at the present time is to strip standing oaks, leaving the trees without bark for a year until they are felled. A tree is scored at regular intervals of some 24 inches with a bark knife. Vertical slits are then made and large semi-cylindrical plates of oak bark are levered off. As tannin is soluble in water, the plates of bark have to be stacked in such a way that rain does not penetrate into the stack. Barking was a task often undertaken by women and children, who sold the bark to the tanneries.28

One of the most unpopular tasks at the tannery was that of grinding oak bark, for the fine dust emanating from the water-driven bark mill penetrated everywhere. The large, dried plates of oak bark were taken to the mill and fed into the hopper of the grinder, which was driven by the water-wheel. The plates were pushed down between the rapidly revolving cutters of the mill.

The bark shed at a tannery was a high building, which at the hey-day of tanning was kept full of ground and unground bark. The building had slits in the walls to ensure adequate draughts, so that the plates of bark were thoroughly dried before grinding. The ground bark was carried from the mill in large baskets to the leaching pits where the tanning liquor was made by adding cold water to the bark, and allowing the mixture to stand for some weeks before use. The tanning liquor in various strengths was then pumped to the tan pits proper.**29**

Oak Bark Drying   *Courtesy: Museum of Welsh Life*

Suspending, Handling and Laying

The method of tanning heavy hides consisted of the progression of butts through a series of pits containing liquors of varying strength, starting with the weakest solutions. The first series of eight pits were the suspenders, and in these pits containing the weakest solution in the tannery, the butts were first placed. Each hide attached to a string which was tied to sticks laid across the top of the pit. The object of suspending was to ensure the uniform absorption of tanning by the pelts when they were transferred to stronger solutions at a later stage. The liquor in the suspender pits was stirred gently at frequent intervals, and the hides were moved daily from one suspender to the other, the liquor becoming progressively stronger from one pit to the other. The tanner had to be very careful that the hides did not touch one another in the suspender pit, as they would display touch marks or be of uneven colour.**30**

At the end of the suspender stage, the butts with all traces of lime removed would be soft and porous, and they had to be laid flat to straighten out creases, before being placed in the next set of pits: the 'handlers' or 'floaters'. Here the hides were laid flat rather than suspended and were moved from one pit to the other at regular intervals of two to three days. There could be up to 12 handlers, containing progressively stronger liquors. During the first two or three of handling, hides were turned over in the liquor with the aid of tanning hooks at least twice a day so that the liquor penetrated the hide fully. A bucket-full of finely ground oak bark was often added to the tanning liquor in the last three or four handlers, while in some cases bark was sprinkled evenly on the hides before they were immersed in the pits. The handling of butts took from six to eight weeks, but at this stage only about a third of the substance of each hide had been fully tanned. To distribute bark evenly throughout the pit, a long-handled wooden plunger was used, while hides were moved from one handling pit to other by means of long-handled tongs or hooks.31

The spent liquors in the first two or three handlers were then pumped back to the suspenders and new, stronger liquors pumped to the last handling pits. The hides were then passed to the final set of pits: the layers, which contained the strongest liquors in the yard. Each hide was sprinkled with oak bark to a depth of about one inch. Bark was first spread on the bottom of the pit and a butt placed over it. This was followed by another layer of bark, then a butt, until the pit was tightly packed. Tanning liquor from the leaching pits was then pumped into the layer pits. The butts were left undisturbed in the first layer pit for some six weeks until the tanning and animal fibre combined. They were then taken out, stratified with bark again and placed in the second layer pit, containing a stronger solution of tanning liquor. Depending on the thickness of the hide, the process of layering could go on for as long as 18 months; indeed occasionally hides were laid away for as long as three years before they were fully tanned.32

After removal from the layer pits, the fully tanned hides were washed in a weak solution of tanning liquor and any particles of tanning materials that still adhered to the pelt were brushed off with a stiff brush. In some cases the wet hides were placed over a device called a 'wooden horse' and the bloom removed with a 'striking pin'. This was a three-bladed triangular draw knife and it was pressed firmly over the grain side of the hide until all traces of tanning liquor had been removed. In other cases the wet hide was placed on a scouring stone table and the bloom from the grain side removed with a piece of stone called a 'scouring stone'. The grain was wiped with a cloth and a thin coating of linseed or cod liver oil was applied over the grain surface of the leather to prevent the too rapid drying of the surface.33

The process of drying itself demanded considerable care, for if the drying were too slow, a mould would grow on the tanned hide. If, on the other hand, the drying were too quick, the leather could be discoloured, hard and brittle. The drying room with adjustable wooden weather boards ensured good ventilation and the gentle movement of air currents to dry the hides as they hung from the racks. Unfortunately, the drying room was also very dark, but it was extremely important that the hides were not subjected to direct sunlight, as this too could damage the texture and colour of leather. After the skins had been partially dried, perhaps for a week or 10 days, they were taken down from the drying racks, damped and piled in heaps, with sacks in between each hide. This was the process of 'samming' or tempering the hides to a moist and uniformly soft condition. They were then submitted again to the process of striking with the pin and then rolled. The roller consisted of a brass cylinder surmounted by a heavily weighted box truck and a long wooden handle.

The butt was laid flat on the solid and level wooden bed, coated with sheets of zinc and the roller was passed over the butt repeatedly until the creases had been removed. After the first rolling, the butt was again hung for some days, it was re-oiled and rolled. This process of oiling the flesh and grain side, rolling and drying could be repeated a number of times. After drying, the tanner's work was complete, but before a piece of tanned leather could be sold to the boot-makers, saddlers and other craftsmen, it had to pass through the hands of another craftsmen, the currier.34

Currying

Currying was to a large extent the mechanical operation of cleansing, reducing in thickness and softening the leather and the impregnation with oils and fats.35 Of course, there were considerable differences in tanning the various categories of hides. The above description was the general method adopted for processing cattle butts for sole leather. Sole leather could be finished by the tanners by rolling and oiling, but other types had to be sent to the currier for finishing. Although after the mid-19th century, oak bark as the main tanning agent used, other agents of vegetable and chemical origins were added to the oak bark. Some of the tans helped the tanning process and vegetable matters such as sumac (the shoots and leaves of a mediterranean tree), quebraco (a South American timber) and valonia (acorn cups from Mediterranean oaks) were often added to the oak bark, particularly after 1860. Non-tans in the form of chemical elements were also added occasionally, and although these did not tan the hides, they served a useful purpose in that they slowed down the rate of tanning, enabling the tans themselves to penetrate right through the hide.36

Apart from bark mills, water-power was used in other leather industry processes; the River Wandle chamois-leather mills used five hundredweight hammers, driven by water-wheels, to pound piled skins of leather in oil baths to attain softness, which was a particularly noiseless operation.37

References

1. P. Carrington, 'Chester' (Chester: 1996), pp. 82-83.
2. ibid., pp, 82-83.
3. Chester City Record Publication, 'Guildhall' (Chester: 1992), P. 3.
4. ibid., p. 10.
5. ibid., p. 16.
6. ibid., p. 10.
7. ibid., p. 15.
8. J. McN. Dodgson, 'The Place-Names of Cheshire`, p50.
9. J.G. Jenkins, 'The Rhaeadr Tannery' (Cardiff: National Museum of Wales - Welsh Folk Museum, 1973), p. 3.
10. ibid., p. 3
11. ibid., p. 4.
12. H.R. Proctor, 'The Making of Leather', (1914), p. 121.
13. J,W. Waterer, 'Leather Making and Leather-Working Tools', in J.G. Jenkins (Editor), 'Traditional Tools And Equipment', (1965), p. 40.
14. J.G. Jenkin, 'The Rhaeadr Tannery', p. 7.
15 Chester City Record Office, Assembly Book A/B/3 f174v
16. J.G. Jenkin, `The Rheadr Tannery`, p.7.
17. ibid., p. 8.
18. ibid., p. 8.
19. Proctor, 'The Making of Leather', p. 23.
20. J.G. Jenkins, ' The Rhaeadr Tannery', p.9.
21. ibid., p. 9.
22. ibid., pp. 9-10.
23 Chester City Record Office, Assembly Book A/B/3 f174v
24. ibid., p. 11.
25. ibid., p. 11.
26. ibid., p. 11.
27. ibid., pp., 11-12.
28 ibid., p. 12.
29. ibid., p. 12.
30. ibid., p. 12-13.
31. ibid., p. 13.
32. ibid., p. 13.
33. ibid., p. 15.
34. ibid., pp. 16-17.
35 Procter, 'The Making of Leather', p. 121.
36. J.G. Jenkins, 'The Rhaeadr Tannery', pp. 16-17.
37. W.H. Prentis, 'The Snuff-Mill Story' (Mitcham: Private Publication by Wilfred Henry Prentis, 1970), p. 78

Tanner and Currier
Bewick Woodcut

Paper Mills

History of Papermaking

The Paper-Maker

The water turns my mill wheel round,
Where rags to paper pulp are ground:
Their snowy leaves on felt I lay,
And squeeze the water well away,
And then I hang my sheets to dry:
All white, and shining like the sky.

by Hans Sacks, about 1550

Paper has a long history. The Ancient Egyptians laid strips of papyrus reed pith in layers at right angles and squashed it to create a type of paper board before 2500BC. However, it is accepted that true paper was first made in China, out of such materials as old rags, fishing nets, mulberry and hemp, around the beginning of the Christian era. The technique of making it was guarded as a state secret for hundreds of years, and paper was exported via the Silk Road. In 751 AD Arabs occupied Samarkand and learnt the art of papermaking from Chinese prisoners. Paper mills were established in Baghdad by 794AD and in Cairo by 900AD. It was brought to Europe by the Moorish conquerors of Spain who set up a mill at Xativia in about 1150. Not until 1490 was there a paper mill built and working in Britain and, even then, our own industry grew slowly. William Caxton's development of printing at Westminster increased the demand for paper, but at first the market was supplied from mills from the Continent, especially Holland and France. It is known that Caxton was not able to use English paper for his first books. In fact, there is no evidence of continuous paper production in the British Isles until 1588 when John Spilman, a German paper maker, began to work a mill at Dartford in Kent, but from this date onwards a number of mills became established on a regular basis. Most were within 30 or so miles from London.[1]

By the late 17th century, paper mills began to spread across England and Wales. However, there was still a concentration of mills in the South and Southeast and most were quite small with never more than four vats working. (The word `vat` used in this way refers to the two or three-man production unit).[2] It is probable that the rate of increase which carried the total number of paper mills from 100 to over 200 mills between 1690 and 1712 slackened from that time, and that the check was imposed by the effects of the Excise duties which were levied in 1712 and increased in 1714.[3]

Paper mills existed at Chester for over one hundred years, from the late 17th century to the early 19th century. In 1696/7, Thomas, son of Edward Thompson, paper maker, was recorded in 'Chester Freemen'.**4** A.H. Shorter asserts in 'Paper Mills and Paper Makers in England 1495 - 1800', that the earliest proprietors or master paper makers at Chester are not known.**5** However, in 1698, the Handbridge Paper Mill was included in a conveyance of property from Hopkins and Hadley to eight Chester gentlemen. This paper mill occupied accommodation previously used for fulling, and was called the Lower Fulling Mill, which worked alongside the Higher Fulling Mill.**6** In 1713, George Scott, paper maker, took apprentice a Sam Deane. In 1721, Thomas, son of Robert Farrington, paper maker, was recorded in 'Chester Freemen'.**7** De Lavaux's map shows that there were paper mills in Handbridge as late as 1745.

Evidence exists that there was a paper mill at the Dee Bridge Mill in 1774 and that a second paper mill which existed at Chester, at Skinner's Lane or Crane Street Mill, was not known until 1791.**8** In 1766, the will of Joseph Bage, paper maker, was recorded. No change in the name of the proprietor or master paper maker at Bage's Mill (which was probably at Dee Bridge throughout the period) was known until after 1800. In 1774, there was an accident at Bage's paper mill at Dee Bridge.**9** In a deed of 1776, relating to the water corn mills, John Bage and John Bosley (Bozeley) were both included as holding properties in Bridge Street.**10** In 1780, James Nuttal ran away from Joseph Bage, paper maker.**11** In 1781, William Bage was recorded as a paper maker at the 'Bridge'. In 1782, Joseph Bage was recorded as a paper maker at the 'Bridge'. In 1791-92, Mr. Bozeley (Bosley) was a paper maker at the 'Bridge'.**12** In 1802, the partnership between Joseph Bage and William Cross, paper manufacturers, was dissolved.**13** In 1756, Robert Bage held a paper mill and corn mill under one roof at Elford in Staffordshire.**14**

Circa 1791, Bozeley was a paper maker at Chester. This is the earliest reference which may be definitely connected with the second paper mill at Chester (on the city side of the river). In 1796, Thomas Bozeley, paper manufacturer, insured the stock and utensils in a paper mill in Skinners' Lane. He probably held the mill until 1801. In that year his will was recorded at Chester, in which he was described as a paper manufacturer.**15**

Up to the beginning of the 19th century all paper was made by hand, using a vat and a hand mould. (Wood-pulp paper was not invented until 1844 by F G Keller.) The raw material from which the paper pulp was derived was essentially rags. The limitations of this batch type of process are obvious, and the demand for paper, which had been increasing with the spread of printing, was eventually satisfied by the Fourdrinier machine and cylinder mould. Henry Fourdrinier developed a machine in the early years of the 19th century in which the pulp was fed continuously on a moving belt of gauze through which water was allowed to drain. Successive squeezing eliminated further water from the web until it was strong enough to support itself, when it passed to a series of steam-heated rolls that eliminated the remaining undesirable moisture. A modern paper making machine is usually of this basic Fourdrinier type, often several hundred feet long.**16** By the mid-19th century, the paper making industry became focused on a relatively small number of large production units, and hundreds of the small mills closed. Although steam power had been used in paper mills at Chester by 1802,**17** these mills had closed prior to 1851.**18**

Rags make paper,
Paper makes money,
Money makes banks,
Banks make loans,
Loans make beggars,
Beggars make rags. **19**

The Siting of Paper Mills

The distribution of 18th and 19th century paper mills, in the period before the industry became focused on a relatively small number of large production units, was based on several primary factors.

A source of rags was a major requirement, so the proximity of a large urban centre was essential, and this centre also provided a market for the finished paper. Chester was attractive because it was not only a market town but also a port, with the availability of both imported and local supplies of rags. At certain mills the paper makers were temporarily faced with local opposition. The plague which had come with the rags led to an order in 1636 for the closing of paper mills in Middlesex until the contagion was removed.**20**

Chief among these primary factors was a supply of water needed in great quantities for processing and power; the water had to be clean and had to have a good fall and reasonable continuity. It was thought desirable that a mill should be situated at the mouth of a valley so that there would be a good flow of air through the drying-lofts. Chester met all these requirements, and the River Dee passing between two low hills now occupied respectively by the city of Chester and its suburb Handbridge, formed a natural valley.

A factor which drew paper makers to certain regions or localities was the possibility of easily and cheaply converting mill sites, and labour which had hitherto been occupied in industries which were now locally entering a period of decay. The collapse of the woollen industry in several districts meant that numerous fulling mills were available for conversion. These were often well suited to the paper makers' requirements in respect of the method of using water power. Also part of the mill gear or fulling stocks could be used for mashing fibres. The conversion of Handbridge Fulling Mills to paper mills was a typical example.

Another factor, was the possibility of sharing accommodation with other kinds of mills, the Dee Bridge Mill at Chester had corn mills and paper mills under one roof. The advantage of sharing accommodation was that the 'vats' were not in daily operation, and labour could be employed on other types of work in the mills.

Raw Materials and Labour

There were a large number of 17th century rubbish collectors engaged in sorting old rags along with every other sort of junk. Rags would be first divided between woollens, which went back to the spinners and weavers for the manufacture of the cheap woollen cloth called 'shoddy', and the cottons and linens which could be used for paper. There were rag merchants and middle-men between the collectors and the mills, who sorted rags into a great number of subsidiary grades - each commanding its own price for both home and export sale. One of these grades, prized because the string cotton made strong paper, was *Mallett's Pinks* - corset cuttings.**21**

Skilled labour was provided by journeymen, so-called because they would travel from mill to mill as chances of work occurred, working in one place perhaps until a stock of rag had been converted into paper. Other jobs were likely to have bee carried out by local part-timers, spared for some months from salmon fishing or the harvest, or by the mill owner and his immediate family. It should be noted that the word `mill` simply implies a source of power, from whatever source, and the same wheels might well be used successively to process rags or paper, to drive a pair of grindstones, or to power a fulling mill.**22**

In the beginning the British paper industry was largely devoted to the production of *Browns,* paper for wrapping and rough work generally, while the well established Continental mills supplied the demand for the finer printing and writing papers.**23** In 1666, there was a proclamation forbidding the import of blue paper, which was used by *sugar bakers and others.***24**

Kingman's 1791 map of Chester shows *Sugar Houses* on the New Wharf, adjacent to the Little Roodee. It is interesting to speculate whether the Chester paper mills produced blue sugar paper in addition to brown paper.

Water Powered Paper Mills

No contemporary sketch of an early British paper mill has been found, but a composite drawing of a German mill dated about 1662 may be used to illustrate the chief processes involved in paper making in a primitive one-vat mill.

After being sorted, cut and washed, and allowed to ferment, the rotted rags or other cellulose materials were placed in water-laden troughs called mortars and were macerated into pulp by a battery of iron-tipped wooden stamping hammers (D and E). These were lifted and dropped by means of cams (C) fitted to the main shaft (B) which was worked by water power, here developed by an undershot wheel (A), which was the same sort of wheel used at Chester. The 'stuff' resulting from this beating process was placed with water in a vat (G) and kept lukewarm; it was agitated by means of a pole or potching stick, which towards the end of the 18th century was replaced by a mechanical paddle called a 'hog'.**25**

From the pulp the vatman formed a sheet of paper by inserting a wire-meshed mould of the required size and giving it a series of shakes, so drawing off the water and causing the fibres of the pulp to inter-twine and form a matted layer on the surface of the mould. As each sheet of paper was thus formed, it was taken off the mould and laid by the coucher, alternately with a sheet of woollen felt, to form a pile. When complete - usually it consisted of six quires or 144 sheets of paper - this 'post' was put in the screw lever press (F), and as much water as possible was squeezed out. After being air-dried on lines (ropes covered with horse-hair or cow-hair which did not stain the paper), the sheets were sized (if the paper was to be made capable of taking ink), and were pressed, dried, and finished.26

The maximum labour force in a single-vat mill probably consisted of a number of women and children to prepare the materials and to sort and pack the paper, a vatman, a coucher, a layer (to separate the sheets from the felts), a man to press, a man at the mortars or engine, and a finisher. In the mills that were small and cramped, conditions of work must have been arduous, particularly for vatmen, because of the heat of the vat, the constant dampness, and the continuous physical strain involved in the monotonous repetition of shaking motion by which the paper was formed on the mould. Poor ventilation in a raghouse could give unpleasant conditions also for those who did the sorting, dusting, and cutting of rags.27 At a paper mill in the nearby Clywedog Valley, old buttons from the rag sorting can still be found mixed with the gravel on the entrance drive, where the rags had been sorted outside.

Possibly in the late 17th century, but certainly by 1740, the Hollander beating engine had been introduced into several English mills. During the second half of the 18th century the engine replaced the older stamping method of beating materials, and by 1800 there were very few English paper mills where the hammers and mortars were still in use.28 This beater consisted of a drum within which there was a rotating wooden roller fitted with iron or steel blades or bars and driven by water power. The rags, mixed with water, were shredded to a pulp between the roller and a bedplate which was also fitted with blades.29

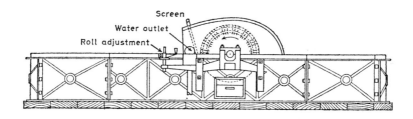

A Hollander Beating Engine   *From `Paper Making in the British Isles`*
Courtesy: David & Charles

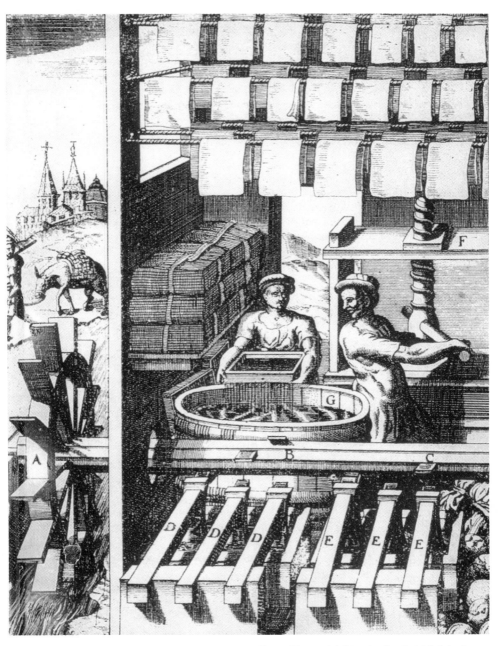

Water Paper Mill, c1662
Courtesy: David & Charles

From `Paper Making in the British Isles`

References

1. Wookey Hole Caves Ltd, Information Sheet, 'The Mill - Papermaking by Hand', p. 1.
2. ibid., p. 1.
3. A.H. Shorter, 'Paper Making in the British Isles' (David & Charles: Newton Abbot, 1917), pp. 75-76.
4. A.H. Shorter, 'Paper Mills and Paper Makers in England 1495 - 1800' (Hilversum, Holland: The Paper Publications Society, MCMLVII), p. 149.
5. ibid., p. 149.
6. 'The Causeway Mills in Handbridge', 'Cheshire Sheaf', Vol. XLIX., January, 13, 1954, p. 3.
7. Shorter, 'Paper Mills and Paper Makers 1495 - 1800', p. 149.
8. ibid., p. 149.
9. ibid., p. 149.
10. Cheshire County Records Office, Deed, Ref. D/3589/1-6.
11. Shorter, 'Paper Makers 1495 - 1800', p. 149.
12. Chester City Records, Poole, 1791-92 Chester Directory and Guide, p. 25.
13. Shorter, 'Paper Makers 1495 -1800', p. 149.
14. Shorter, 'Paper Making in the British Isles', p. 69.
15. Shorter, 'Paper Makers 1495 - 1800', p. 149.
16. Cossons, 'The BP book of Industrial Archaeology', p. 212.
17. Shorter, 'Paper Making in the British Isles', p. 110.
18. ibid., p. 134.
19. R. L. Hills, 'Papermaking in Britain 1488 - 1988' (London: The Athlone Press, 1988), p. 145.
20. 'Paper Making in the British Isles', p. 22.
21. Wookey Caves Ltd., Information Sheet, p. 1.
22. ibid., p. 1.
23. ibid., p. 1.
24. Shorter, 'Paper Making in the British Isles', p. 23.
25. ibid., p. 14.
26. ibid., p. 14.
27. ibid., p. 14.
28. ibid., pp. 38-40.
29. ibid., p. 38.

SEE CHAPTER ON WATER SUPPLY

Boring Machine for Wooden Pipes - the original `trunk` lines.
At the top can be seen how the tapered end of one pipe fitted the next.

Snuff Mills

The Origins of Tobacco

Smoking is believed to have its origins within Central America where it was practised some 2,000 years ago by the Maya tribe. They were known to have smoked tubes of loosely rolled tobacco leaves, similar to the present day cigars. Later the Aztecs in Mexico are known to have incorporated smoke inhalation in their religious rituals, and further south the Arawak Indians of the Amazon valley observed similar customs. Soon after the discovery of the West Indies and the American continent, numerous accounts were written of the New World people who smoked tobacco and also used it for chewing and snuffing. In the West Indies, Brazil, and Central America natives rolled small leaves of tobacco, wrapping them in a larger tobacco leaf or in a maize or palm leaf - the prototype of the cigar. In Mexico, tubes made of various substances were used like a cigar, and further north the pipe was the receptacle, made of clay, marble or even lobster claws.1

The Oldest Existing
Illustration Of A
Smoker: A Maya God

Reproduced By
Kind Permission of
Imperial Tobacco Ltd.

Smoking came to Europe with the return of Columbus from the New World. He had been offered some dried leaves as a token of friendship and his men had witnessed how these leaves were used. In fact one of the returning sailors, Rodrigo de Jerez, was reported to have been imprisoned for smoking on the grounds that he was *consorting with the devil.*2 The introduction of tobacco seeds or plants is attributed to Ramon Pane, Columbus' priest on his second voyage. It was many years later, in 1560, that Jean Nicot, after whom the herb was given its botanical name 'Nicotiana', sent a gift of seeds to the Queen Mother of France, Catherine di Medici, recommending the plant for its curative properties. Accounts of many other explorers have illustrated the widespread use of tobacco on the American Continent and the West Indies and there is little doubt that these men introduced tobacco to Spain and Portugal around this time.3

The Rise of Smoking in Britain

Once introduced to Europe from the west the use of tobacco spread rapidly. Most European countries adopted snuff in the first place and smoking later. In Britain smoking came first, to be succeeded by snuff-taking, which after a long period of time, gave way to smoking. By 1560 snuff was well established at the French Court and even more generally established in Spain. In England tobacco was a late arrival.4 Various people have been credited with being the first to smoke in England. It is known that tobacco was introduced into Britain at some time before 1565, when Henry Hawkins returned from a voyage to America. Sir Walter Raleigh is believed to be chiefly responsible for making the addiction fashionable, but despite the claims by men of rank and position the title of first to smoke in England should probably go to a humble sailor of Bristol who, as early as 1556 ...*did walk through the street emitting smoke from his nostrils*. 5

By the end of the 16th century pipe smoking was a nationwide habit and, in this age of voyages of discovery, the smoking addiction travelled around the world. In a short space of time men of all colour and creeds were smoking tobacco. That smoking developed in this country more rapidly than any other was largely attributable to Sir Walter Raleigh's influence and example. The apothecaries who first sold tobacco had to increase their stocks to meet growing demand, and around 1600 special tobacconists shops began to flourish with tobacco also being sold at public houses, grocers, chandlers, drapers and even goldsmiths.6

Opposition to Tobacco

Tobacco was fast becoming an important commodity but even then it had powerful opponents. The smoking habit was denounced by the clergy, and the literary world contributed to this satire and lampoon. The climax was reached in 1604 when King James 1st published his famous `Counterblaste to Tobacco` in an effort to stop smoking, which he personally hated. He also saw it as an opportunity to discredit Raleigh whom he despised. The import duty was increased from the modest 2d of Elizabethan times to *6/10d per lb*. In France, Louis XIII prohibited the sale of tobacco except where medically prescribed, and in some Eastern nations smoking was punished by torture and death.7 In 1634, the Czar of Russia, Michael, decreed that for the first offence smokers should be whipped, and for the second offence executed, while snuff takers were to have their noses amputated.8

Meanwhile English farmers continued the large scale cultivation of tobacco. James, therefore, prohibited local cultivation of the plant on the grounds that it would reduce the growing of food, but in spite of this farmers carried on planting and harvesting their crops.9

There was much room for criticism about the production of tobacco and snuff, particularly taking into consideration the adulterations then in common use - leaves of rhubarb, dock, burdock, coltsfoot, beach, plantain, oak, elm, cabbage, lettuce, as well as peat, bran, sawdust, meal, and so on. Fairholt mentions a case where a cigar manufacturer successfully resisted a legal penalty for making *Havana Cigars from tobacco on which duty had not been paid* by proving in his defence that he never made use of tobacco leaf at all.**10** As late as 6th March 1809, evidence was given in a letter of a poor lady who died from the effects of adulterated snuff:

James Hill,
137 St. Martin's Lane

Dear Mr. Urban,
...I know a lady who took the cancer in her nose and died, that had been in the habit of taking snuff. The doctor that attended her insisted that there were particles of glass in the snuff she had used visible to the naked eye, and that these, having been strongly pulled up, had lodged in the cartilages and bones of the nose, and caused the disorder. On analysing it, he found that rotten wood, pieces of old coffins etc., ground down and mixed with powdered glass, red and white betony, and other cheap cephalicks constituted the chief ingredients in the snuff she had bought and used... **11**

In 1614, King James, finding himself once again in financial difficulties, decided to take the importance of tobacco into his own hands and granted two traders the sole power to import tobacco, on the condition that they paid him £3,500 for the first year and £7,000 every year thereafter for 10 years. In 1624 he decreed that imported tobacco should be landed only at the Port of London. Traders at Bristol and other ports resorted to smuggling on a grand scale and during the years that followed considerable duty was lost. In 1638 the Government changed their minds and allowed the landing of tobacco at Bristol, Plymouth, Dartmouth and Southampton, but not Chester. In the meantime, despite the various statutes which had been introduced, growers in England continued to ignore the law. On several occasions troops were ordered to burn the tobacco fields in Gloucestershire, the main centre of cultivation. By the end of the century, however, local production had virtually ceased because of the better quality and cheapness of Virginian tobacco which smokers preferred.**12**

One possible reason for the continuance of the addiction in the face of such opposition was the reputed power of tobacco to combat outbreaks of plague which periodically attacked Europe at that time. It is said that during the Great Plague of 1665 the boys of Eton were requested to smoke in school every morning, under the supervision of a master, and were soundly whipped if they failed to do so. Eventually rulers around the world discovered, like King James, that the revenue to be obtained by the state from tobacco was more important than the physical or mental damage to their subjects.**13**

City Treasurer's Accounts (Shrove Tuesday) 1703
`paid for Bread, Tobacio and pipes 5s6d`

Chester City Fire Regulation 1709

...order'd that the....Mayor of this city... cause of the fflaxdressers and hostlers in this city to be solemnly admonished that they do not smoke any Tobacco or suffer the same to be smoked...in their respective fflax shops or stables.

By the early 1700s the use of tobacco had attained a substantial degree of popularity. It was estimated that over a period of seven years from 1702 to 1709 the aggregate consumption in England and Wales was 5,112,339 kilos, or about a kilo per head of population. It is surprising therefore that the initiative for proper manufacturing was not seized by the people wholly concerned with tobacco. Instead, it seems to have been taken up by grocers such as Stephen Mitchell and & Son, E. & W. Anstie Ltd of Devizes, and Franklin, Davey & Co of Bristol (wine and spirits).**14** In 1782, Chester, J. & W. Nicholls were tobacconists & grocers in Watergate Street, and Moulson and Eddowes were tobacconists in Eastgate Street.**15**

Snuff

At the start of the snuff-taking era in England, which coincided with the reign of Queen Anne, it became popular to attend a snuff-taking academy much as it had once been essential to study the art of the fan. Here would be taught the ceremony of the snuff box, rules for offering snuff to a stranger, a friend or a mistress, with an explanation of the careless, the scornful, the politic and the surely pinch and the gestures proper to each of them. During this period a young gentleman felt inadequate without his snuff box, it was as necessary a part of is attire as his gold-topped cane. Of course, they could be combined, the snuff being carried in the gold top.**16**

Many ladies became addicted to snuff - the more fastidious took snuff from the back of a fingernail or used a tiny spoon or nose-shovel instead of a quill as before.**17** A lady called Margaret Thompson was so addicted to snuff that in her last will and testament she requested that:

*... I be buried with such quantity of the best Scotch snuff (in which I always had the greatest delight) as will cover my deceased body... Six men to be my bearers, who are known to be great snuff takers in the parish of St. James's, Westminster and instead of mourning, each to wear a snuff-coloured beaver... Six maidens to bear my pall, each to wear a proper hood, and to carry a box filled with the best Scotch snuff, to take their refreshment as they go along... The minister to walk before my corpse and to take a certain quantity of snuff... I also desire that my old friend and faithful servant, Sarah Stewart, to walk before the corpse to distribute every 20 yards a large handful of Scotch snuff over the ground, and to the crowd who may follow to my burial place.***18**

Incidentally, in the 1660s snuff became known as 'snush'.**19** Also, it may be interesting to note that it was snuff that popularised the widespread use of the handkerchief.**20** The great boost to snuff-taking in this country came at the beginning of Queen Anne's reign, heralding the snuff-taking 18th century. The British fleet, under Sir George Rook, making a raid on Port St. Mary, near Cadiz, captured and destroyed some French ships of war and Spanish treasure ships in Vigo Bay. Among the spoils were hundreds of casks of fine Havanna snuff, 50 tons of which were distributed among Rook's seamen as a *prize*. This huge quantity of snuff was sold at the principal seaports to the quickest purchasers. The land-sharks drove a hard bargain and wagon-loads were disposed of at the rate of fourpence a pound. It was christened Vigo snuff:

The popularity of the war, the name of the snuff and the novelty of excessive cheapness combined to induce a very general use of it.[21]

Snuff reached its peak of popularity in Britain during the Regency period with the Prince Regent and Beau Brummel the leading exponents. It cannot be assumed of course that snuff production necessarily predominated over pipe tobacco manufacture during the rest of the 18th century but many pipe producers did go to the wall during this period. The increasing population swelled both the volume of pipe and snuff users. In 1775 exports of Virginia and Maryland tobacco to Britain reached the quite astonishing total of 4,585,400 kilos.

The first years of the 19th century saw snuff maintain its popularity within the upper classes. Gradually the number of snuff-takers grew fewer and by the end of the 19th century the number dwindled to a minority. There was still sufficient to support an unobtrusive, but flourishing British snuff industry and this remains true today.[22]

Snuff Manufacture

Snuff is basically a tobacco product. Quite simply it is powdered tobacco, with the addition of mineral salts, and flavour additions of natural products and oils. Originally, manufactured snuff was not easy to come by and Do-it-yourself snuff-makers used a carrot-shaped plug of tightly-wrapped leaves and a rasp to hand-grind their own powder.[23] Before heavy duties were imposed on importation of tobacco the whole leaves were used. When taxes made snuff expensive, the best part of the tobacco leaves were reserved for smoking and the waste, stalks and roots were used for snuff. The stalks were called the *hard parts* and the root was called the *carrot*.[24]

Nicholl's Tobacco & Snuff Mills, Established 1780.   *Courtesy of L Morgan*

The craze for snuff taking swept Britain and meant importing on a vast scale to cope with the demand. The Coroner's Inquisitions at Chester tell of the deaths of two men in the tobacco trade: in 1657/8, Robert Carr fell from a boat bringing tobacco from Dawpoole in dark and stormy weather **25** and in 1670, Joseph Foster, tobacco cutter, died from natural causes whilst in the Northgate Gaol.**26** From 1720 onwards, snuff mills were established in London, Bristol, Kendal and Sheffield.**27** However, the Chester Snuff Mills predate these by about two decades, as evidenced by report of a fire in Mr Topham's Chester Snuff Mills in 1701.**28** J. & W. Nicholls and Moulson and Eddowes had tobacconist shops in Chester in 1782. Even after the establishment of water-mills for snuff making there were still many people producing snuff by hand.

Thomas Nicholls & Co Advert, Probably late 19th Century

The main method of industrial milling was with a large shallow bowl built up of elm and sometimes lined with copper. The bowl was revolved by the water-wheel and a stone wheel ran inside the bowl using the edge for grinding, unlike the wheels for corn-grinding whose flat faces were used in pairs. The tobacco was continuously forked into the wheel-cum-bowl contact and ground to snuff. Snuff milling stones usually were made from light coloured millstone grit and were 1.2 metres in diameter and 30cm or so thick. The snuff was sifted twice by the 'dressers'. One man worked each machine. Prior to grinding, the tobacco was dried in a brick kiln fitted with copper-covered shelves on which the tobacco was stacked. The fire was underneath the kiln and the flue passed outside the drying chamber in order not to taint the drying tobacco. An experienced man was needed for the drying process, because he had to know which part of the leaves to cook most and for how long, some softer parts needing less drying. The objective was to bring the tobacco to a crisp state without over-drying for correct grinding.**29**

In the larger mills there was a more sophisticated snuff-milling arrangement, which consisted of a number of mortars with revolving pestles. The mortars were deep bowls about 45cm in diameter by 40cm deep made from elm. The aperture of the hollow bowl at its top was a little smaller in diameter than the lower part, and the top of the bowl was dished. A pestle in the form of a tapered baton revolved in the bowl on a loose fixing so that impinged on the sides of the bowl when it revolved. Tobacco was placed into the mortar to be ground. The revolving pestle caused the powder to work its way upward onto the dished top of the mortar, where it was collected by the miller. There could be as many as 12 mortars, fixed firmly in a large round table with 12 revolving axles above, on which were fixed the pestles. A central large horizontal cog wheel, driven by the water-wheel, in turn drove the 12 axles. Two men would work at one table, and there may have been several mortar tables in a large mill. The assemblage of heavy wheels and pestles with the water-wheel would make quite a rumble. In 1914 this was noticed by one writer:

> *Leaving the village by the path across the marshes west of Mitcham church, the low rumble of a water-wheel betokens a mill at work and the fragrance shows that it is grinding snuff.***30**

Snuff Mill Working Conditions

Working conditions were very unpleasant in a snuff mill:

> *Men often had time off, several days sometimes, particularly in the last century (19th) and before that, employers' grumbles on the habit are on record down the ages. It may have been that with the long hours and the hard work, the men just could not keep up with it... The actual working of the machines by the millers was not very comfortable but in spite of that some of them did it all their lives and knew no other work. The milling of anything was a trade to be learned and the experience learned tied a man to it. The air of the mill room was thick with tobacco dust and paper hats were worn and sometimes a cloth over the nose. Men would go out to lay on the grass in front of the Mill Cottage for a respite and in hot weather Mr. Hatfield would close the mill for a while. Once the mill was closed for six weeks because the heat made the smell of snuff overpowering, the men were put on other work... Every ledge and every surface in the mill was piled with dust similar to a saw-mill and the sweepings from the floor were considerable. No mention is made as to whether this dust was made use of. Although the snuff dust did not do permanent harm to the workers (Prentis's opinion), some men could not stand it long even with wet sponge respirators... The dust problem was there every day for the millers and anyone else whose duties took him into the mill. They emerged covered from head to foot with the powder...The inside of the mill is gloomy: large floor areas with inadequate windows and more especially so when, as is, or was usual in industrial premises, they were unclean, and still more especially so when the mill was filled with the milling machinery...***31**

Tobacco Leaf Shredding at Nicholls`, C20th   *Courtesy of L Morgan*

"Rare Old Chester"

By 1903, Thomas Nicholls & Co. had stopped producing snuff. However, demand for tobacco products was enormous and Nicholls' price list of 1909 covered a wide range of tobacco products including; packet shags, fancy packets, dark shags, special chewing shags and pressed tobaccos. Brand names included; *Union Jack*, *True Blue*, *Jolly Miller*, *Chester Cut* and *Oliver Twist*. In the 1915 price list there appeared *Rare Old Chester*, a popular brand which continued to be produced until the Handbridge works closed down in the 1950s.

The Hand Painted `John Peel` Vans at Nicholls`   *Courtesy of L Morgan*

References

1. 'Imperial Tobacco Limited, London', 'The Tobacco Story' (London: Imperial Tobacco Limited, 1996), p. 1.
2. ibid., p. 1.
3. ibid., p. 2.
4. 'Imperial Tobacco Limited, Liverpool Divison', An unpublished paper - 'A Short History of Snuff' (Liverpool: 1995), p. 2.
5. 'The Tobacco Story', p. 2.
6. ibid., p. 2.
7. ibid., p. 3.
8. 'A Short History of Snuff', p. 3.
9. 'The Tobacco Story', p. 2.
10. 'A Short History of Snuff', p. 3.
11. W.H. Prentis, 'The Snuff-Mill Story', p. 93.
12. 'The Tobacco Story', p. 3.
13. ibid., p. 4.
14. ibid., p. 4.
15. Broster, 1782 Guide, pp. 82 & 100-101.
16. 'The Tobacco Story', p. 8.
17. ibid., p. 8.
18. 'Snuff & Nonsense'in 'Imperial Tobacco Review',Vol.4, No.3 May 1962. p2.
19. ibid., p. 2.
20. 'The Tobacco Story', p. 8.
21. 'Snuff & Nonsense', p. 2.
22. 'The Tobacco Story', p. 8.
23. 'Snuff & Nonsense', p. 2.
24. 'The Snuff-Mill Story'. p. 135.
25. Chester Record Office, 'Coroner's Inquisitions', QCT/11/1a. Feb 1st 1657/8, Death of Robert Carr.
26. ibid., QCT/12/27, 25th Dec. 1670, Death of Joseph Foster.
27. 'Snuff & Nonsense'. p. 2.
28. Chester City Records Office, 'Cuttings', Ref. 072714, Aug 20 1701.
29. Prentis, 'The Snuff-Mill Story', pp. 135-136.
30. ibid., p. 139.
31. ibid., p.139-140.

Various Brands of Tobacco   *Courtesy of L. Morgan*

Flint Mills

Followers of Fashion

The Romans brought the craft of making glazed earthenware to Britain. This technique was revived in the medieval period. Western ceramics were also influenced by rare occurrences of expensive Chinese porcelains, which 'trickled' to the West via the Middle East. During the Middle Ages there were examples of coloured lead glaze ware, and a rich dark-glaze was also found on redware from the Cistercian houses such as Fountains Abbey. The major importance of these Cistercian wares was that they were produced in relatively fine-walled drinking vessels. Prior to the 15th century, ceramics were not generally used for small drinking cups. The 16th century saw the introduction to England, from the Netherlands, of tin-enamelled earthenware, later called 'Delftware'. In the same century, another type of earthenware called 'Slipware' was made in Kent and Staffordshire. In the 17th century, the introduction of expensive porcelain from China and the vogue for the new exotic hot drinks, tea and coffee, were the spur to European pottery development. The first London 'Cophee House' opened in 1652. In 1660, Samuel Pepys recorded: *I did send for a cup of tee (a China drink) of which I never had drank before.* A century later imports of tea exceeded 2.27 million kg per year. In 1775, Samuel Johnson recorded, in his dictionary: *TEA   A Chinese plant, of which the infusion has lately been much drunk in Europe.* At first, tea was served in red stoneware teapots. Cups, imported with tea from China by the Dutch and English East India Companies, were made in the 'mysterious' and expensive blue-and-white porcelain. The British potters' challenge was to make home-produced, cheaper substitutes.[1]

John Dwight 'Master Potter'

In the 17th century, while Continental potters tried to make porcelain, the Englishman, John Dwight of Fulham, took out two patents (1672 and 1684) for fine 'Stoneware' (which he called porcelain). From 1660 to 1665, he resided in Chester, as secretary to the Bishop of Chester. He was a lawyer, having studied Civil Law at Oxford. Between 1662 and 1665, three of his children were baptised in St Oswald's Church, Chester. From 1666 to 1671, Dwight lived at Wigan, Lancashire, in the office of Secretary to the Bishop of Chester and as Diocesan Registrar. Among his duties were acting as ecclesiastical lawyer, travelling on circuit with the Consistory Court of the Archdeaconry of Richmond. While at Wigan, he experimented with clays and tried to make porcelain and stoneware. Charles Leigh, a contemporary historian said of Dwight:

I was informed from my ever-honoured friend Sir Roger Bradshaw of Haigh, that it was upon a whitish yellowish Earth, in a Field near the Kennel-Pits at Haigh, that Mr Dwight made his Discovery of his most incomparable Metal...[2]

In 1668, John Wilkins was made Bishop of Chester; then in 1669 he brought a Chancery action against Dwight for mishandling Diocesian funds. Some time after

March 1671, encouraged by *Mr Boyl and Dr Hook*, Dwight moved to London and by 1673 he was making pottery at a *riverside* location in Fulham.**3**

In 1690, the Elers brothers produced similar wares at Fulham and thereafter, in Staffordshire. Elers ware was unglazed but, since it was fired at high temperature (1200 C), it was not porous and, unlike delftware, not vulnerable to hot liquids. Various factors contributed to a steady improvement in stoneware, which made it very different from the coarse grey stonewares of 16th century Germany and Flanders.**4**

John Astbury of Staffordshire

In Staffordshire, pale Shelton clays were used in the first steps towards a finer white-bodied ware, and eventually a fine white salt-glaze stoneware evolved from a white-burning clay mixed with fine grit and sand. It enjoyed great popularity during the 18th century, being hard, translucent and as near to porcelain as could be reached short of the real thing. John Astbury (1688-1743) of Stoke-on-Trent, was instrumental in developing this ware and also in using ground flint (silica) in the body material as a whitener.**5** There is a bizarre story, which attributes the discovery of the use of ground flint to John Astbury:

In 1720, Astbury was journeying to London on horseback when at Dunstable he was forced to seek assistance as his horse was going blind. An ostler effected a remedy by burning a flint pebble, grinding it to a powder and blowing it into the horse's eyes. This benefited the horse, and Astbury noticed the pure white colour of the dust and its clay nature when wet. On his return to the Potteries he experimented with the new material. At first it was used to produce a dip coating for clay ware. With improved transport, the imported flint became cheaper and it was introduced into the clay body itself. It gave strength, whiteness and prevented shrinkage during firing to produce a hard cream coloured product. **6**

The addition, to the clay, of calcined flints gave stability in the kiln, durability and whiteness. About 1715, the important discovery was made that Devon and Cornwall yielded a particularly pure china-clay. Ball-clay, a fine white pipeclay originally imported in ball form from Devon and Dorset, was added to give greater plasticity and strength; and felspar was added as a flux. The remaining problem was surface texture. Most unglazed stoneware was too rough; lead glaze detracted from appearance; saltglaze was better, but nevertheless had an orange-skin surface.

In the 1720s, it was discovered that stoneware ingredients, if fired at the much lower temperature of 750 C, produced a useful cream-coloured earthenware. A clear lead glaze was then evolved which, applied to this ware as a liquid dip and replacing salt-glaze, produced an ideal body that, under the name of 'Creamware', came to displace saltglaze and other wares, not only in Britain but on the Continent and in America, for a century. It had the advantage of being both light and strong, and it was attractive to look at, whether painted, transfer-printed or left undecorated.**7**

Randle Sorton, Entrepreneur

Lyn and Maurice Hillis state in 'Chester White Ware Manufactory', that while the greatest production of 18th century white salt glazed stoneware was undoubtedly concentrated in the Staffordshire Potteries, similar wares were also produced at a number of other ceramic centres including; Rotherham, Derby, Benthall (Shropshire), Bovey Tracey (Devonshire), Liverpool and Chester. Although there is no local tradition that pottery was made in Chester, clay pipes were manufactured here from at least 1646. Before the year 1700, twenty-five Chester pipe makers had been recorded. The Chester pipe makers were dependent upon white firing clays imported from Devon and Dorset. It was not unreasonable, therefore, that an attempt was made to produce salt glaze stoneware at Chester, a city into whose port pipe clay was regularly shipped.

In addition, rock salt was readily available from Cheshire, coal from Flintshire and flint was obtainable from North Wales or from further afield via the Port of Chester. Skilled potters were probably recruited from outside Chester. Although Buckley pottery centre was only eight miles away, the dozen or so potteries located there only made items such as slipwares, mottled wares and black glazed wares. The salt glaze expertise needed may have come from Staffordshire or perhaps Liverpool.[8]

Direct evidence of the production of stoneware in Chester is given in 'Williamson's Liverpool Advertiser' in 1757:

> *"Chester White Ware Manufacturer Messrs Randle Sorton & Co.*
> *Proprietors of the White Ware Manufactury,*
> *have opened their Wharehouse near the Bridge in the City of Chester*
> *and sell all of*
> **White Stone or Flint Ware**
> *made at their works and not inferior to any done in Staffordshire.*
> *Both Wholesale and Retail Samples sent to any gentleman or ladies*
> *in the Country that will pay the Carriage and a good*
> *allowance for Shopkeepers and Exportation.*[9]

Randle Sorton was a wealthy Chester merchant. He became a freeman of Chester in 1721, being doubly qualified as: *son of Wm. Soreton Clerk and a apprentice of Joseph Soreton of Chester, wetglover*. Although he was variously described as a wetglover, skinner or merchant, he appears to have had other interests outside the leather trade, in addition to potting. He died in 1778, leaving a considerable fortune.[10]

The description "near the Bridge" in the advertisement appears to refer to the Handbridge side of the River Dee:

*The district on that side of the bridge was then known then and now as Handbridge, and in the mid-18th century was the scene of a number of industrial enterprises such as lime kilns, a copperas works, paper making and snuff mills.*11

At that time, the Handbridge mills and industrial area lay within the bounds of two parishes, St. Mary's-on-the-Hill and St. Bridget's. Evidence for the existence of potters living in Handbridge was provided by the parish register of St. Mary's:

William Son of Wm. Morrice Potter & Ann his wife of Handbridge was bap. this 17th day of September 1758.

Thomas Son of Robt Lloyd & Katherine his wife of Handbridge was Baptized the 25th day of March 1759.

Hannah daughter to Robt. Shaw Potter & Hannah his wife of Handbridge was Baptized the 6th day of January 1761.

Jane daughter to Robt. Shaw Potter & Hannah his wife of Handbridge Bapd. 15 day of April 1764.

The Registers for St. Bridget's contain the following entries:

Charles, Son of Charles Hankey, Mug Man baptized April 29th 1759.

Ann, Daughter of John Meachin, Mug Man baptized Aug. 19th 1759.

The Hillis's maintain that these Handbridge potters had well known Staffordshire names, and that the description *Mug Man* was somewhat ambiguous and could conceivably be applied to a seller rather than a maker of pots. However, it is significant that the two entries were in the parish of St. Bridget's, in which the Handbridge White Ware Manufactory was located, and it is likely that Hankey and Meachin were employed at the potworks. The entries in the parish registers indicate a working period for the potworks extending to at least 1764,12 while a lease and release of 1777, between Henry Tharp of Chester, Button Maker and Joseph Ackerley of Mickle Trafford, refers to:

*Those several Dwellinghouses or Cottages and Workshops with the appurtenances of him the said Henry Tharp situated and being in Handbridge ... near to & adjoining a certain lane there called Paper Mill Lane on the south side ... and also a large oven with Funnel or pipe erected and being in the yard on the back side of the said premises ...formerly made use of as a pottery for the burning and firing of Mugs ...And also all that new erected workshop warehouse or building aforesaid on the south side ...were or some part or parts thereof was or lately made use of as a pottery for making and Manufacturing of pots and Mugs ...*13

In a further lease of 1786, Edward Ommaney Wrench, leased the same property to Joseph Ackerley, on the surrender of the former lease to Henry Tharp. The same details concerning the property were given and on the back of the document appeared the following:

...it was agreed that ...the said Joseph Ackerly ...shall not be obliged to repair or rebuild the Buildings hereto fore Used as a pottery for the purpose of Making

*Earthen Ware but shall be at liberty either to preserve the said Buildings or to take down the same...*14

These two documents fix the site of the pottery in Paper Mill Lane in Handbridge. The 1777 lease describes the pottery in the `past` tense, which implies that pottery production had ceased. This is confirmed by a 1779 Fire Policy issued to Tharp's workshops, stock and utensils in Paper Mill Lane.15 In 1777, it appeared that Tharp's bone-cutting business occupied most of the premises mentioned in the leases, which leads to the assumption that the pottery had ceased to operate.

The maximum working period of the Handbridge White Ware Manufactory appears to be about 1757 to 1776. The Hillis`s maintain that the demise of Handbridge potworks probably came about because it was isolated from the rapid growth of industrial potting in Staffordshire, and was unable to follow developments leading into creamware, and its simple stonewares became unwanted.16

Archaeological Evidence

Extensive renovation of a row of four small, early 19th century cottages in Mill Street, Handbridge between October 1984 and 1986, revealed traces of a small pottery-production site, in operation in the mid-to late 18th century. Part of a brick-built, circular kiln base was excavated, and a quantity of kiln furniture and wasters (waste pottery from the kiln) was recovered. Products of the pottery included white salt-glazed stoneware, lead-glazed creamware and possibly brown salt-glazed stoneware items.17

Flint Mills

The purpose of a flint mill was to grind its products to a consistent fineness and avoid contamination. Flint pebbles are hard and dark and provided an unlikely source of ceramic material. However, when calcined their crystalline structure breaks down, forming a soft white cristobalite. The process consisted of placing flint pebbles into a kiln in alternate layers with coal. When lit, the induced draught rapidly raised the temperature of the flint. Initially, water was driven off and the flint became friable and at 1,000 degrees centigrade was converted to cristobalite. Allowed to cool naturally the pebbles were drawn by hand from the bottom of the kiln and sorted from the small quantity of ash remaining.18

Originally, the flint was ground by millstones, but as they were expensive and wear was excessive this practice soon ceased. Stamp mills, consisting of heavy vertical timber shod at the bottom with iron were tried. They were raised and dropped, by means of cams on a shaft driven by a water wheel, and flint pebbles were shovelled under them. Apart from problems of contamination of the product, silica dust was given off in large quantities. Workers began to die from what was later to be called "Potter's Rot". When it became clear that a worker's life could be as short as three to four years, it is not surprising that men would no longer do this work.

Flint Mill

*From 'The B P Book of
Industrial Archaeology,
1987 David & Charles.*

*By kind permission of
the publishers.*

In 1726, Thomas Benson of Newcatle-under-lyme took out his first patent for grinding flint under water to minimise the dust. This invention used two large iron wheels running on their edges followed by grinding with large iron balls. The problem with this process was that iron particles discoloured the pottery on firing, so his patent of 1732 replaced the iron with edge runner stones and balls of stone. From this process the widely used 'pan method' method of wet grinding developed.**19**

A circular pan of about 3.7 metres in diameter was constructed with vertical sides about one metre high. The floor was carefully built using stone blocks. A central vertical shaft was gear driven from a water wheel. From this four or five horizontal arms or 'sweeps' rotated around the pan with vertical hanging arms pushing around blocks of stone 'runners' up to half a tonne in weight. These runners were prevented from contacting the pan side by a circular iron ring; the slug iron, which was attached to the outer hanging arms and rotated with them. Typically, a charge of about one and a half tonnes of flint plus water was added to the pan and the runners rotated for 24 hours. This was enough to grind most of the flint to the required fineness. The mix was run off to a washtub, where more water was added. The tub was a cylindrical tank, with a vertical timber gate allowed to pivot in the centre. The gate was rotated to agitate and separate the particles which tended to coagulate.**20**

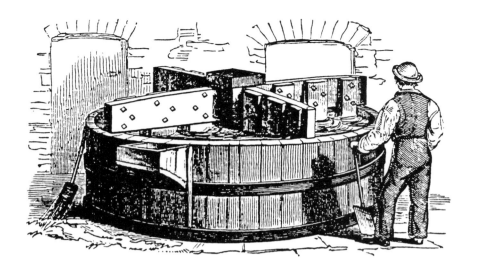

Flint Pan

From `The BP Book of Industrial Archaeology` 1987
David & Charles. By kind permission of the publishers.

This simple grading process allowed the course particles to sink and be pumped back to the pan for regrinding. The finer particles rose and were run off to brick built settling tanks or arks. To achieve an accurate separation the liquid could be run over a fine sieve. Often an empirical judgement was made regarding the distinction between fines and oversize particles. In the arks, the excess water was removed. In the side of the ark was a vertical plank containing a series of wooden bungs. As the particles sank, bungs were knocked out from the top to draw off clear water. The thickened slop which remained could be run into barrels for sale, or if it had to be transported over any distance, it would be run to the drying kiln. The drying kiln was a low sided brick tank built over flues running from a coal fire to a chimney stack. The water was evaporated and the flint cake cut into blocks for sale. The potter would again add water so that the flint could be thoroughly mixed with other constituents. After processing the excess water was removed by a filter press . The resulting clay was then ready for use.**21**

At first glance, there appears little connection between pottery and needle making. However, on the demise of the White Ware Manufactury around 1776, the redundant flint mill could have been reused for needle making. The name Sorton is associated with both the pottery and needle making industries. In 1781, William Sorton was a needle maker in Bridge Street and then, in 1782, in Handbridge.

References

1. M. & G. Payton, 'The Observer's Book of Pottery & Porcelain'
(Frederick Warne & Co. Ltd.: London, 1973), pp. 10-11.
2. R. Edwards, 'London Potters circa 1570-1710' in 'Journal of Ceramic History' No. 6 (Stafford:
George Street Press, 1974), p. 56.
3. ibid., p. 56.
4. 'The Observer's Book...', pp. 11-12.
5. N. Cossons, 'The BP book of Industrial Archaeology' (David & Charles:
Newton Abbott, second revised edition 1987). p. 165.
6. B. Job, 'The Grinding of Flint and Bone' in 'Journal of the
Staffordshire Industrial Archaeological Society' (1989), p. 1.
7. M. & G. Payton, 'Pottery & Porcelain', pp. 10-11.
8. L. & M. Hillis, 'The Chester Whiteware Manufactory', 'Northern
Ceramic Society Journal', 4 (1980/1), 43.
9. ibid., p. 39.
10. ibid., p. 39.
11. ibid., p. 40.
12. ibid., pp. 40-41.
13. Chester City Record Office, CR49/29.
14. Liverpool Record Office, Coleman Deeds, Cheshire Deed 63.
15. Chester City Records Office, Sun Fire Policy No. 357543, CR49/31.
16. Hillis, 'Chester White Ware', p. 43.
17. 'Cheshire: Chester, Handbridge', in 'Post Medieval Archaeology' (1986),
Vol. 20, p. 353 and 'A Note on an C18th Pottery Site in Mill Street, Handbridge, Chester' in
Cheshire Archaeological Bulletin' (1986-unpublished), No. 11, p. 1.
18. B. Job, 'The Grinding of Flint and Bone' in 'Journal of the Staffordshire Industrial
Archaeological Society, 1989, p. 20.
19. ibid., p. 20.
20. ibid., pp. 20-23.
21. ibid., p. 23.

Needle Mills

Chester Needlemakers

The 'Freeman Rolls of Chester', 1392-1805, list only one needleman - William Hall of London, needleman, son of Henry Hall of Chester, innholder, who was admitted to the freedom in 1694.1 Randle Holme, the Chester Herald, writing in the 'Academy of Armour' (1668) listed the range of needles available at that time. Two William Lowes, father and son, worked at the needle-making trade in the 17th and 18th century. The father was apparently imprisoned in the Northgate Gaol as a Quaker in 1685.2 In 1781, a Mr Sorton was recorded as a needle-maker in Bridge Street.3 In the same year, the marriage of William Salt, needlemaker of St Mary's parish, was recorded in Holy Trinity's parish registers.4 In 1782, William Sorton was a needle-maker in Handbridge.5

The earliest reference found to the Chester needle mills to date, is in a deed of 1790, which included *William Evans (Needle Maker)*.6 Mrs Butler and William Evans were both needle and fishhook-makers in Handbridge in 1791/92.7 William Evans was again recorded as a needle-maker in Handbridge during 1795.8 In the 1819 election five needle-makers voted, three of whom lived in Handbridge.9 The last record of needle-making in Chester, found to date, is for a Thomas Evans, needle-maker in 1822.10

There is a reference to the Old Needle Factory in the 'Chronicle' of 1 Oct. 1887:

Fall of a house into the Dee. The Rector of St. Mary's wishes to state that he will gladly receive and distribute any contributions that may be sent him towards the relief of the families who have been rendered homeless and lost all their goods by the fall of a house into the river in Lower Handbridge.

An appendage manuscript note added that:

*the house here noted is the Old Needle Factory at the west side of the south end of the Old Bridge. It partially fell during a high tide in September, and this month (July or October?) the remainder is being taken down.*11

This may have been the site of a small mill with a single waterwheel to the west of the bridge.12 The Chester Chronicle of 1834 advertises a *Needle Factory adjoining the Snuff Mills... formerly occupied by Mr Joseph Evans.*13

The Pre-History of the Needle Mills

According to John G. Rollins, in his book The Needle Mills (1970), there is little doubt that improved methods of needle-making were introduced, towards the end of the 14th or early 15th century, into the vale of the River Arrow by the Cistercian monks of Bordesley Abbey. Possibly the monks used water-power to carry on some of the more arduous processes of the craft, but there is no evidence to support his theory. However, according to Rollins, it is logical to suppose that so advanced a community would utilise the power already harnessed for other purposes - fulling stocks for cloth manufacture, furnaces and forges for the production of iron, and later paper mills - in the production of needles. **14**

Needle-pointing on rapidly revolving grinding stones, scouring under heavy elm runners, and polishing on buffs, immediately suggest themselves as processes admirably suited to prime-mover adoption. Some support may be gained for the idea from the fact that needle-makers settled themselves in communities in the vicinity of bridges, actually occupying properties on them in some cases. Examples are the needle-makers of Wilton (1250), London (1593) and Chester (1786): all had water-power available to them from the mills either actually under the arches of the bridge themselves, as in the case of London Bridge, or adjacent to the bridge as at Chester.**15**

All the mills used the same production methods including the needle mill at Chester and those around Hathersage in Derbyshire.**16**

Processes

Pointing

It was almost impossible to obtain a true point by the old hand-work methods of hammering (snobbing) and filing (fettling), nor could satisfactory results be obtained on a slowly rotating grind-stone such as were generally used to sharpen ordinary tools. In order to obtain the desired result, a high-speed stone had to be used, which posed a problem. Several expedients were tried including treadles, dog-wheels, like those used to turn cooking spits, and large hand-turned wheels connected to much smaller ones by means of a rope or catgut (warps). Later, light section leather belts were used for this purpose but proved too costly to be put into general use. In any case, the speeds obtained were far too slow to produce really satisfactory results and were used solely to set the points of needles on completion.

In the quest for greater speed a rocker frame was devised that became known as the "Whee-Wah" from the noise it made when in operation. The "Whee-Wah" was constructed in the form of a light gate and was suspended from a beam above the operator's head by means of gate-hooks and bands, which enabled it to swing freely to and fro. The frame was provided with a connected rod, known as a sweep, which operated a driving wheel, and was found to deliver a higher and more uniform drive to the pointing stone, while at the same time enabling the labourer to continue working for longer periods without undue fatigue. Later still in 1690 some of the more successful needle-masters installed horse-gins manufactured in Worcester for the purpose.**17**

The London needle-makers developed a water-driven machine for pointing needles. These machines were so dangerous to operate that, in 1623, a complaint was made against their use to the Privy Council, resulting in their ruthless suppression. One such machine was broken up in 1629 and the needle-maker was arrested.**18**

The pointing of needles on high-speed power-driven sandstones was introduced into the trade about 1780. The 'new' process was almost certainly similar to the one developed by the London needle-makers a hundred or so years earlier, and just as deadly. The first stones used were pieced with a square hole and fitted tightly onto a square shaft. This was accepted practice for edge grinders at the time, but it was found that at the high speeds required to obtain a good point the stones tended to crack in the corners of the holes under centrifugal force and break-up, causing serious injuries and sometimes death. Disturbing as this was, it was not the worst aspect. The dust given off during pointing soon proved a killer. The pointers worked in semi-darkness in order to see the points forming by the light of their own sparks. The whole time they were enveloped in clouds of dust. The life of a pointer was considered to be about seven years, few surviving to see their 30th birthday. They were well paid and refused any improvements in their working conditions for fear their earnings would be cut.**19**

Runner Scouring

The next great development in the needle trade was the application of water power to the very heavy process of needle scouring. Runner scouring is a method of polishing needles ideally suited to water power. It is thought that this method was introduced into Britain towards the end of the medieval period from the north of Italy, where it

Needle Pointing   *From the `Penny Magazine`, January 1843*

was employed to give the bronze needles of the region their characteristic lustre. The process was very simple and has remained basically the same up to the present time. The needles were first made up into bundles about as thick as a man's wrist, eyes all one way, points the other. The bundles were then placed together in a tight leather pouch which was filled with abrasive material such as pumice powder or marble paste, lubricated with olive oil to make a grinding paste. The end of the bag was then secured and the bundle placed on the floor under a large flat stone and rolled backwards and forwards for a considerable time. When it was judged that the process had been completed, the bag was opened and the needles removed. They were washed and dried prior to inspection, damaged needles were removed, and any others that did not reach the desired standard were repacked and subjected to a second scour. The interaction of the needles and the abrasives had a two-fold effect: it produced a high gloss finish on the needles and straightened them at the same time. Later in Germany c1370, the same process was applied to iron and steel needles with equal success before being introduced into the English Needle Region (the Midlands) about 1375.[20]

Quartzite pebbles were calcined and ground to powder to provide abrasive. Sharp pit sand and silver sand were also used both in this country and in Europe. Malleable clay was mixed with water to a smooth paste and found to be a good substitute for oil but was replaced by soap. It was found easier to wrap the needles in leather skins rather than pouches, which in turn gave place to course canvas, hessian or a heavy grade of sacking known as burlap. The large flat stones as used in Italy were almost unobtainable in the needle district and were replaced by heavy elm boards known as runners. At first the runner was operated by the feet of the needlemaker while he worked at his bench. Then the German system was introduced whereby the runner was placed on a table and pushed to and fro by children. A later idea put the runner on an inclined plane did not enjoy popular support because the work was too hard for children and had to be undertaken by adults.[21]

The next development was the adoption of the "Whee-Wah" which enabled a man to operate two runners; one at table height and a second below. About this time the practice was adopted of putting, under each runner, two bundles which then became known as a sett. Today a single bundle is called a sett. The horse-gin was first used for needle scouring when Needle-master Biddle installed one in 1698 at his mill in Sambourne to operate two frames of runners each, sometimes known as a scouring horse. Later, yokes of two horses and, in the case of William Steward's mill at Reddich, three horses were used. It would appear that the horse-mills of the Reddich district were never fully successful, owing to the fact that the turning-circles were too small (often less than 6 metres) to permit a horse to develop its full power.[22]

The "Whee-Wah" predated both the horse-gin and the water-wheel and all three continued to be used right up to the introduction of steam. The wheel appeared to be used in London in 1623 and possibly earlier, and was introduced into the Midland Region by 1685. The "Whee-Wah" would seem to be a native development about 1650 and not a foreign innovation.[23]

Scouring   *From `A Short Description of Needle-Making` by A E Morrall, 1886*

References

1. The 'Cheshire Sheaf' (11,208), 1964, p39.
2. ibid., p. 40.
3. Broster, Chester Guide and Directory, 1781, p. 18..
4. the 'Cheshire Sheaf' (11208), 1964, p40.
5. Broster, 1782, p. 82.
6. Cheshire County Records Office (C.C.R.O), Deed, Ref. D/3589/1-6.
7. Poole, Chester Directory and Guide, 1791/92, pp. 25-27.
8. Broster, 1795, p. 79.
9. The 'Cheshire Sheaf' (8962), 1948, p. 6.
10. The 'Cheshire Sheaf' (11208), 1964, p.40.
11. Cheshire Sheaf 1948 (8967) pp 6-7.

12. D Bethell, `Portrait of Chester` (London: Robert Hale, 1980), p.152
13. Chester Chronicle 8th Aug 1834.
14. J.G. Rollins, The Needle Mills (London: Society For the Protection of Ancient Buildings, 1970), p. 3.
15. ibid., p. 3.
16. ibid., p. 3.
17. ibid., p. 4.
18. J.G. Rollins, Needlemaking., (Shire Publications: Aylesbury, 1981), pp. 3-4
19. ibid., pp. 25-26.
20. J.G. Rollins, 'The Needle Mills', p. 6.
21. ibid., p. 6.
22. ibid., p. 7.
23. ibid., p. 7.

Tyrer`s Tower: Detail from SW Prospect of Chester, 1728
By S & N Buck,   *Courtesy of The Grosvenor Museum*

Water Supply

Adam's Ale

People have often associated water with the supernatural. The soldiers of the 20th Legion, part of the Roman forces which conquered and then occupied Britain for over 400 years, took due care to erect an altar beside the aqueduct which they constructed to carry water from the spring at Boughton to the fortress they were building at Chester: this they dedicated to *Nymphis et Fontibus* - to nymphs and springs. The Roman technology, largely destroyed or left to ruin in the Dark Ages, was not equalled in sophistication for over 1,500 years.

The Roman aqueduct took the form of an open channel or an underground line along which the water flowed by gravity into a reservoir. From there it was distributed by different outlets to communal fountains, public baths and private consumers. Public baths were a feature of any Roman site, civil or military. The Romans also had a system for disposing of waste water. Rain water and used water drained into stone channels and followed the fall of the land into the River Dee.1

Monks and Abbots - Early Water Pioneers

The religious communities were more concerned than most for their personal hygiene and were careful to ensure that there was always enough water on tap for the 'lavatorium' or wash-place (from the Latin 'lavare': to wash). The north cloister of Chester Cathedral contains a long stone shelf in its north wall: this was the lavatorium which the monks used before meals in the refectory. It probably had a stone or lead trough to contain the water. They dried their hands on linen towels which, according to their rules, they were not to use for removing dirt or blowing their noses.2

It was unlikely that the spring water that the monks used would be anything but clean, because they took the trouble to conduct it to their communities from distant sources by means of pipes. The lead pipes which the Romans had laid in Chester's Eastgate Street had long been abandoned and forgotten when, 1,000 years later, the Christian Abbot of St Werburgh organised the piping of water from a spring at Christleton. He had to obtain a grant from the spring's owners, the Burnel family, and the permission of King Edward I to push pipes through the city's walls. A reservoir *20 feet* square was constructed to hold the water from the Abbot's Wells at Christleton, and another one inside Chester Cathedral cloisters known as the *Preece* or *Sprice*. Remains of the earthenware pipes which connected the two, and for which part of the city wall had to be demolished and rebuilt, were discovered some 600 years later when workmen started digging the foundations of a house at Barrel Well Hill in 1814. They were some *four feet* deep and *half a yard* long. Another water pipeline was laid in the reign of Edward I from a spring near the Gallows at Boughton to the Black Friar's house.3 Permission for this pipeline was given in 1276. It would appear that certain orders of friars seemed to have had a special talent for constructing such water supply systems and are mentioned more than once in historical records.4

Public Water Supply

In 1536, when the smaller religious foundations were suppressed in Chester, the city authorities took over the water supply systems they had built for themselves, and adapted them to serve Chester's citizens - a transfer which took place all over Britain.5 Water was also supplied to the city by the Water Leaders (or Drawers of Dee). In 1587, although they had a large membership, their petition for a charter was refused.6

In 1537, Dr. Wall, a prebendary of the cathedral, organised the building of a new conduit from the spring at Spital, Boughton. This new conduit was to have lead pipes and carry water to the Bridgegate. It soon proved unequal to the demand and further alterations were started. In 1549, the conduit was thoroughly inspected and responsiblity for its upkeep given to the Murengers (a body appointed to keep the walls of the city in good repair).7

In 1569, the council laid down regulations to deal with outbreaks of fire in the city. Each alderman and councillor were to be responsible for a number of large buckets to carry water to the scene of any fire. In the same year, the conduit in Bridge Street was covered in.8

As demand for water increased with a growth in population, other sources of water were sought. In 1572, an attempt was made to sink a well in the middle of Northgate Street, but after reaching *13 fathoms* no water was found. In 1573, it was decided to bring *a man from London* to build a conduit from the Dee to the High Cross. A committee of 12 men was appointed to discuss terms, and the *expert* was selected to carry out the work for £200 (see Water Power).9

However, the city's supply of water remained erratic. It was proposed that a conduit be built to the High Cross. The end of the *waterworks* was a large tank or cistern of lead or stone into which the water poured itself, and out of which, by free-flowing spout or a controllable tap, it poured into a stone basin below. That was all there was to a waterworks in those days. The system worked entirely by gravity - *gravitational works*. Its head was placed prominently in a public place with easy access for the people. It was given a substantial, stylish housing in keeping with the important role it would play in the life of the town. Its decoration would remind its users of the people by whose public-spirited charity it had been built. The house for the cistern placed at the High Cross in Chester in the 1580s bore the arms of the city, the Earls of Derby and Leicester, Mr Offley and Dr Wall.10 It was planned to tap more springs at Boughton to increase the flow to the High Cross. A Mr Trew planned to achieve this objective and requested a payment of £100 down and an annual salary as long as the water supply progressed satisfactorily. The money was subscribed voluntarily by the citizens, with the Mayor setting an *example*.11 Over the next decade there were frequent references to amounts of money paid out to workmen for maintenance on the conduits. There seems to have been some degree of individual plumbing by a William Sanderson who piped water directly to the houses of Richard Bavard, John Radcliffe and others.**12**

Water Power

The carrying of water from conduit head to consumers' premises, whether in buckets and tankards or in water carts, was slow and unreliable. The only people happy with this system were the water carriers who, not surprisingly, resisted change. However, change had to come, because the carrier-based distribution could not keep pace with the growing demand for water throughout the 17th century.

Water Cart   *Bewick Woodcuts*   *Water Carrier*

Reliance on the force of gravity alone to move water from source to head was also becoming a severe brake to growth. The answer was to find an effective means of raising water in bulk to a height from which it could then flow to its point of delivery. There was really only one solution. Since the location of the city or town at the receiving end was fixed, the water had to be moved upwards. The power human muscle could exert unaided was limited. With a mechanical device such as an Archimedes Screw, however, it could be greatly increased. The screw was devised in Egypt around 1000 BC, and improved by the Greek mathematician Archimedes, who died about 212 BC. It introduced the idea of raising water by 'pumping' - 'sucking' it up through a cylinder, which needed very much less exertion than lifting it in a container. It consisted of a spiral screw (originally of leather or lead) wrapped round an axle which could be turned by the crank at the top of it. When the bottom was placed in water, and the screw turned, the water was taken up to the top.**13** However, this device would only have supplied a limited amount of water.

Animal power was another option. Horses and donkeys could be made to walk round in a circle, harnessed to the horizontal wooden spigots or rotor, geared to turn a vertical wheel which wound up a rope with the bucket on the end full of water.

However, it was still laborious and slow. Horses, donkeys and oxen, like human beings, grew tired, hungry, needed rest and feeding. They could easily be worked to death. The wind, which could exert a force of up to 10 horsepower on the sails of a windmill on a hill, had no such weakness; but whether it blew or not was beyond human control. Even so, all workable methods of raising water were tried.**14**

As mentioned earlier, in 1573, the Corporation of Chester contracted with an *engineer* from London to provide for the sum of £200, a set of waterwheels at Dee Bridge. They also paid him to maintain the system. Twenty years later, in 1593, an English engineer called Bevis Bulmer obtained, from the Corporation of London, a lease permitting him to erect a 'chain pump' - buckets on a moving chain or belt as opposed to the rim of a wheel - worked by horses at Broken Wharf, to raise water from the Thames for a public supply.**15** However, what could be depended upon to power a bucket wheel or chain non-stop, without tiring, without having to be fed? Running water, the perpetually flowing river that turned the wheels of the watermills. The implication is that Chester was one of the first cities with a water-driven 'chain pump' system.

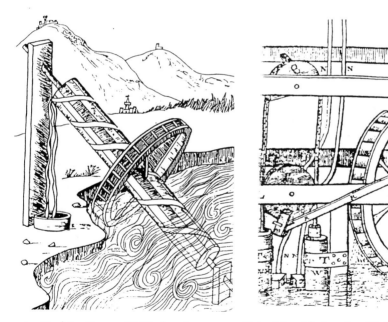

Archimèdes Screw, C16th drawing   *Peter Morris`s London Waterwheel,* **1635**

Water Pumps

Although manpower, horsepower, wind power and river power had been employed to supply water, water engineers still looked for a more efficient and reliable way of raising water. The solution came not from a native source but from a Dutchman who had learned his skills in the Low Countries, where the constant threat of flooding by the sea had concentrated the minds of engineers.

It is not known when the Dutchman, whose name was anglicised to Peter Morris, came to England. By some time in the middle of the 16th century, however, he had won a place for himself in the service of Sir Christopher Hatton (of Hatton Garden), a favourite of Queen Elizabeth. Morris (or Morice) saw the potential for obtaining a more reliable and more substantial water supply from the Thames. In 1574 he submitted a scheme to the Corporation of London for installing a paddle wheel under the arch of London Bridge: the tide running up the Thames would turn it one direction, and the tide running back to the sea the other. The wheel was planned to operate a pump which drew fresh water from the bottom of the river and forced it through a pipe into a cistern on the bank. The Corporation thought the idea would never work, and rejected it out of hand. Apart from anything else, the Corporation had no wish to offend the Rulers, Wardens and Fellows of the Brotherhood of Saint Cristofer of Water Bearers of London, who had drawn up an extensive list of Rules, Ordnances and Statutes in 1496.**16**

Hatton had faith in Morris, and in 1578 he persuaded his royal mistress to give a patent to the imaginative Dutch water engineer:
*who hath by his great labor and charge found out and learned the skill and cunning to make new kind and matter of engine to draw water higher than nature itself.***17**

The 'city' grudgingly gave Morris permission to put a waterwheel and pumps under the last arch of London Bridge on the city side. They gave £50 towards the cost, but had such little faith in the idea that they declined to give him a contract to complete the system. It took Morris two years, and another £100, to build the foundations for the wheel in the river. The Corporation would not support Morris, and so he decided to complete the installation out of his own pocket and prove them that it 'did work'. When it was finished, Morris invited the Lord Mayor and his entourage to a demonstration. They could hardly believe their eyes when they saw Morris squirting water from a hosepipe over the tower of St Magnus Church. The system worked beyond their wildest dreams. In 1581, they granted Morris a lease of the arch for no less than 500 years. The public supply system started in 1582.**18**

The paddle wheel rode on the surface of the river, and was rotated by the incoming and out going tide. It did not turn a wheel or buckets, but a shaft which pulled a disc to and fro which raised and lowered the two plungers of the two pumps below it. This forced the water from the river into pipes climbing up a '128 foot' water turret, and discharged it into a cistern:
*There being strayned through a close wyre grate it descendeth into the main wooden pipe which is layd along the street: and into it are grafted divers small pipes of lead serving each of them to the use of service of particular persons.***19**

104

Of the waterworks at London Bridge at this time, the city's historian Walter Timbs wrote:

*Morice used water-wheels turned by the flood-and-ebb current of the Thames through the purposely contracted arches, and working pumps for the supply of water to the metropolis; this being the earliest example of public water service by pumps to dwelling houses. Previously water had been supplied only to public cisterns from whence it was conveyed at great expense and inconvenience in buckets and carts.*20

Tyrer's Tower

The Chester waterworks had two main similarities with the waterworks at London Bridge: it was sited on a tidal river and was adjacent to the aches of a bridge. In addition, Chester had the added advantage of a constant head of water created by the weir.

In 1600, 18 years after Morris's water engine had entered public service, John Tyrer of Chester was granted permission to lay pipes and build a tower on Bridge Gate in order to supply with water such houses as requested it. He was responsible for any damage caused by the trenching operations and to arrange individual terms with householders. He was told to leave a passage over the Bridge Gate and charged a rent of 5/- for the tower. The high octagonal tower was built and water was raised from the Dee to a cistern in the top and thence to the city:

*The Mayor and Citizens have geven and graunted ... to the said John Tyrer... full power... to break up digg Trench and myne the streets soile groundes of the saide Citie ... for the convenyente and necessarie for the conveying carrying dryving or passing of water in pipes or instrumentes of leade from the River of Dee to any part or partes of the saide Citie and full power... To laie burie place and settle waterpipes and other instrumentes of leade... a Tower or mount over and upon the Bridge gate... Cesterns Ingins or other Instruments for the raising forcing or conveying of water from the said Ryver of Dee to runne or passe in pipes... of lead in the said Citie....*21

'Ingins and forcing' almost certainly refer to a 'Morris' type water engine. Only such a device, at that time, was likely to have provided the power to raise the river water to the considerable height of the Bridgegate tower. Corroborative evidence to support this assumption comes from a book, published in the early 17th century entitled 'A Relation of A Short Survey of 26 Counties', which was observed in a seven weeks journey begun on 11 August 1634, by a 'Captain, a Lieutenant and an Ancient', all three of the 'Military Company in Norwich':

*In our marching the City rounds, wee pass'd ouer 4. Gates, which she dayly openeth to let in both her owne Country-men, and her neighbouring Welsh Shentles [shanties?]: At one of these Gates next the said Riuer, wee tooke an exact view of the rare waterworks, which are Middletoniz'd, and brought vp to a high Tower, on top of the Gate house, and from thence conuey'd by Trunckes, and Pipes, all the City ouer, as in London ...*22

'Middeltoniz'd' refers to Sir Hugh Middleton, or Myddleton, who took over the New River project from Captain Colthurst, who had run out of money. Middleton was an alderman of Denbigh, and Lord Mayor of London, and is famous for his canal to supply London with fresh water, for which he was made a baronet in 1622. He died in 1631.**23**

Tyrer`s Tower, 1600 - 1781   *After Wilkinson*
Courtesy of The Grosvenor Museum

The military men visiting Chester in 1634/35 took an 'exact' look at a 'rare' waterworks 'as in London'.24 In 1622, Tyrer was given another grant to build a tower for a waterworks and well-place *10 feet* square in Spital, with power to convey water to a cistern near the High Cross. This was intended to supply all parts of the City but gradually fell into disrepair.25 In 1634, Tyrer conveyed the Waterworks at the Bridgegate and Boughton, to Sir Randle Mainwaring and others.26

By 1652, after the devastation of the Civil War, the conduit at the High Cross had fallen into disrepair, and it was decided that it should be dismantled and the lead cistern disposed of for the use of the city. The conduit (head or cistern?) was converted into a shop *for the City's profit*. There were also problems with Tyrer's system. The Corporation ordered that the people responsible for its upkeep should declare by 1st May the supply as formerly. It seems that they possibly did, at least until 1673, when Thomas Evans was granted the lease of a piece of waste ground next to the Waterworks at Bridgegate for the erection of an engine to be operated by horses to draw water up the tower from the river during the summer for 99 years at *3s4d* per annum. The demand for water increased steadily and in 1681, the aldermen and JPs inspected a place near the bridge at Flookersbrooke with a view to making a pit to hold fresh water. By 1687, the supply of water was shut off for all but short periods, morning and afternoon.27

Daniel Defoe described Chester's water supply in his 'Tour Thro' the Whole Island of Great Britain':

When I was formerly in the city, about 1690, they had no water to supply their ordinary occasions but what was carried from the River Dee upon horses in great leather vessels like a pair of baker's paniers, just the very same for shape and use as they have to this day in the streets of Constantinople and at Belgrade in Hungary to carry water about the streets to sell for the people to drink. But at this time [early 18th century], I found a very good water house in the river, and the city plentifully supplied by pipes, just as in London is from the Thames; though some parts of Chester stands very high from the river.28

George Sorocold of Derby

The man who contributed more than any other in Britain at this time to the improvement of water engineering was born at Derby in about 1668. As a young water engineer he had been intrigued to learn of a water pumping system which a Frenchman named Rannequin had designed to provide water for the French king's palace and gardens at Versailles. It had 14 waterwheels, operating 253 pumps. Sorocold designed a similar 'forcing pump' and proposed a plan to the Mayor and Burgesses of Derby for bringing fresh water to houses direct. They liked the idea and in 1691 gave him the building known as Gunpowder Mill:

Overleaf **Sorocold`s Water Engine, 1731**   *By Henry Beighton*
From an Engraving in the Museum of London, with their permission.

*with free liberty to erect a water-house, a water-wheel and other engines, laying pipes for conveying water into the streets, lanes and passages within the borough, to hold for a term of 99 years at an annual rent of £3.***29**

The project was completed in 1692 and the installation served Derby for much longer than 99 years, till 1829. Indeed, many of Sorocold's pumping systems continued to work from about 1700 to 1850, when the growth of population rather than inherent defects made other methods necessary. During a visit to Derby, Daniel Defoe commented on what he called a throwster's mill - *the only kind in England* - which was erected, he said, *by one Soracule, a man expert in making mill-work, especially for raising water to supply towns for family use...But he made a very odd experiment at this place. For, going to show some gentlemen the curiosity, as he called it, of his mill, and crossing some planks which lay just above the millwheel, regarding it seems what he was to show his friends more than the place were he was, and too eager in describing things, keeping his eye upon what he pointed at with his fingers than what he stepped upon with his feet, he stepped awry and slipped into the river.*

He fell close to the sluice which let the water in on the wheel and it was difficult for anyone to catch hold of him. The force of the water carried him through and pushed him under the great wheel *which was going round at a great rate*:
> *His body being thus forced in between two of the plashers of the wheel, stopped the motion for a little while, till the water pushing hard to force a way, the plasher beyond him gave way and broke, upon which the wheel went again and, like Jonah's whale, spewed him out, not upon dry land, but into that party they call the apron, and so to the mill-tail where he was taken up and received no hurt at all.***30**

News of the successful fresh water supply which George Sorocold had given Derby soon spread and he was to install his water-engines, reservoirs, conduit heads and pipes in numerous towns all over Britain. Sorocold's name does not always appear in local records of many towns, usually because he did not retain a financial interest in his works once they were constructed, and leases were granted direct to those who intended to carry on as proprietors. However, there can be little doubt that Sorocold was responsible for designing and carrying out the work, although his name may not appear in the records. In some instances no records remain of what actually happened beyond the bare fact that some sort of water supply was installed.**31**

It is true that Peter Morris installed a water supply in London on similar lines, as early as 1582, but Sorocold seems to have been the first to introduce the same principle to many provincial towns. Moreover, Sorocold's wheels were superior to those of Morris, which they superseded at London Bridge Works.**32**

John Hadley

The London Bridge water wheels were designed to rise and fall in accordance with the level of the stream which turned them, a principle patented by John Hadley in 1693. There are no specifications filed with Hadley's patent, which by the way claimed several different inventions, so it is not entirely certain that it was exactly the same device used by Sorocold, although it probably was.**33** In 1696, Sorocold and Hadley were engaged on water engineer, Hugh Marchant's waterworks in St Martin' Lane, London:

*To Thomas Kirke. I have been this day, and am to meet tomorrow, Mr. Saracole and Mr Hadley. I have seen his engine consisting of three mill wheeles with small cranks at each end of the axletree, which raises Tems water, and all are carried by one stream of kennel water... one wheel being under another, I do think the best piece of work I have seen.***34**

In 1701, Sorocold worked on the London Bridge Works, and a detailed description of one of the section of the new works was given by Henry Beighton in 'Philosophical Transactions' (1731):

*The waterwheel was 20 ft. diameter with floats 14 ft. long and 1.5 ft. deep. The wheel was coupled by gearing giving an increased speed in the ratio of 2.2 to 1 to two four-throw crankshafts, one on each side the waterwheel. Connecting rods from these crankshafts oscillated over-head beams, to the ends of which the pump rods were fixed, so that the one waterwheel worked 16 pumps. The pumps had bores of 7 in. and strokes of 2.5 ft. with the waterwheel turning at 6 r.p.m. the pump displacement was about 880 gals. per minute against a head of 120 feet equivalent to a h.p. of 32. The waterwheel could be raised and lowered to suit the state of the tide, a mechanism patented by John Hadley in 1693. This was found to be of little use and was seldom used.***35**

The complete waterworks consisted of four waterwheels driving 52 similar pumps and is said that 11,724 tons (11,912 metric tonnes) of water were raised per day. This equals a water h.p. of 66.**36**

In 1692, the Mayor and Citizens of Chester granted to John Hadley of Worcester, and to John Hopkins of Birmingham, the right to make new works for raising water from the Dee at the Bridgegate. They investigated the possibility of repairing the waterworks but found it pointless and so they started new works. They purchased Tyrer's grant and also one of the corn mills to site the engine and built a cistern at Abbey Court. They also laid pipes from the streets to serve houses. This new system supplied the city for nearly a century **37** The Abbey Court cistern remained in service until 1828, when it was taken down with the 'old shambles' and replaced by another cistern, fixed over the engine-house of the new potato market.**38** Considering the wide spread use of Sorocold's engines (one was installed at Macclesfield) and his close association with Hadley on other works, there is little doubt that a 'Sorocold' water engine was installed at Chester.

In 1698 Hadley and Hopkins conveyed the waterworks to John Williams and others who carried on the works until the first water company with statutory powers was formed in 1826 and the water intake was removed to Barrel Well Hill. The 18th century saw the introduction of new fire regulations by the City Assembly, including:

*Upon notice of any ffire by the Ringing of the ffire bell in this City the Owners of the Waterworks be obliged to cause their Water Engine on the River Dee to be work'd with the utmost fforce, and the water to be directed as much as may be to the place where such ffire shall happen to be.*39

In 1710, the problem of obtaining water from the Dee was underlined, when the proprietor of the waterworks complained about the dumping of rubbish in the river at the bottom of Dee Lane which was being washed downstream into the waterwheel works. The inhabitants of Northgate Street were dissatisfied with their water supply and complained that because of their location and distance from the engine it was insufficient. Consequently they decided to reopen the old draw-well which had been covered over and was in need of repair. They were given a grant to repair it and install a pump at their own expense. The Corporation relented slightly and agreed a grant of £10 towards the cost if the work were completed in three months.40

In 1731, Thomas Dannald, a baker and also the Clerk of the Chester Waterworks, was not as lucky as George Sorocold when he fell:

*Dannald stood upon a plank in the water engine in order to oyl the brasses there he accidently slipped and fell down headlong under the crank belonging to the said water engine by which fall he received a mortall wound or was crushed and bruised by the said crank in such a barbarous manner that he instantly dyed...*41

Chester Waterworks Company

By 1824, the Chester Waterworks Company had four or five shareholders and a new scheme had been proposed for raising more water from the Dee, augmented by the water from Barrel Well Hill. There had been many complaints against the old company for poor service and high charges. A new company was formed to buy the pipes and right of supply of the heirs of Hopkins and Hadley (who had had a right to supply the city with water for *their heirs and successors for ever*). The first waterworks company with statutory powers came into being in 1826 and was the forrunner of the present company. a powerful steam engine with double pumps was built near Barrel Well Hill and apparatus for purifying the water by deposition and filtration. Plans were made for reservoirs on high ground but even so supplies were frequently cut off in time of drought and during high tides.42

In 1950, the West Cheshire Water Order authorised water pumping from the River Dee, and in 1951 the Hydro-electric Power Station, once the site of the Dee Mills, was taken over by the West Cheshire Water Board who subsequently used the site as a pumping station. North West Water Authority continues to pump water to Sutton Hall Water Treatment Works at Ellesmere Port.

References

1. Chester City Record Office, M. Fitzsimmons, J.E. Smith and E. Stell, ' Brief History of the Water Supply in Chester' in 'Chester Waterworks Centenary Brochure' (1967), Ref. P942.714 628.1, p. 1.
2. Barty-King, 'Water: The Book' (London: Quiller Press, 1992)p21
3. ibid., p. 21.
4. 'Brief History of the Water Supply in Chester', p. 2.
5. 'Water: The Book', p. 21.
6. 'A Brief History of the Water Supply in Chester', p. 3.
7. ibid., p. 3.
8. ibid., p. 3
.9. ibid., p. 3.
10. 'Water: The Book', p. 33.
11. 'A Brief History of the Water Supply in Chester', p. 4.
12. ibid., p. 4.
13. 'Water: The Book', pp. 39-40.
14. ibid., p. 40-41.
15. ibid., p. 41.
16. ibid., p. 45.
17. ibid., p. 45.
18. ibid., p. 46.
19. ibid., p. 46.
20. ibid., p. 46.
21. 'Water supply' in 'The Cheshire Sheaf', March 1963 (11,038), pp. 14-15.
22. 'A Relation of A Short Survey of 26 Counties' (1634/35),Gen ed L.G. Wickham (London: F.E. Robinson, 1904) p 50.
23. ibid., p. 159.
24. ibid., p. 50.
25. 'Brief History of the Water Supply in Chester', p. 5.
26. 'Chester Waterworks Centenary Brochure', p. 6.
27. 'Brief History of Water Supply in Chester', p. 6.
28 D. Defoe, `A Tour Through the Whole Island of Great Britain` (London: Penguin, 1986), p. 394
29. 'Water: The Book', p. 63.
30. ibid., p. 62.
31. F. Williamson, 'George Sorocold of Derby. Pioneer of Water Supply', reprinted from 'Derbyshire Archaeological & Natural History Society's Journal', 1936, pp. 66-67.
32. ibid., p. 65.
33. ibid., p. 65.
34. ibid., p. 82.
35. ibid., p. 84.
36. ibid., p. 85.
37. 'A Brief History of Water Supply in Chester', p. 6.
38. Hemingway, 'History of Chester', p339.
39. Chester Record Office, City Assembly Minutes, A/B/3 174v
40 'A Brief History of the Water Supply in Chester', p. 6.
41. Chester Record Office, `Coroner`s Inquests`, QCT/20/17, 17th June 1731, Death of Thomas Dannald..
42 ibid., p. 7.

Bewick Woodcut

Hydro-electric Power Station

Today we take electricity so much for granted that it is difficult to imagine life without it. Not only is electrical energy fundamental to the standard of living of us all but it is also now the major source of power for industry. Electric power has almost completely freed industry from the location factors of the past, which tied it to streams and rivers for power or to the coalfields when steam was the major prime mover. Hydroelectric power, in which water turbines drive the generators, was not much used in Britain because there were few large rivers. In 1894, Worcester Corporation built the "Powick, Hereford & Worcester", the first major hydroelectric installation in Britain. The station closed in the 1920s.**1**

The original Chester Power Station was erected at Crane Street in 1895 and consisted of Direct Current Generators supplying current at a pressure of 210/420 volts. The generators were driven by triple expansion reciprocating steam engines fed by boilers fitted with chain stokers.**2** Public lighting was installed in the first year of operation in 1896, and consisted of 48 arc lamps. The first incandescent lamps were installed in 1899.**3**

Boiler House, Crane Street Works   *City of Chester Electricity Undertaking*

Increase in demand for electricity required the installation of additional generating sets, and by 1910 the maximum capacity of Crane Street Works was reached. The possibilities of water power were investigated and in 1911 work was started on the

Hydro-electric Power Station, situated on the site of the Old Dee Mills (on the bridge), which was purchased by Chester Corporation in 1895. The purchasing and holding rights were set out in the provisional Chester Order 1905, and confirmed in the Local Government Board's Order Confirmation Act, 1905.[4]

The Hydro` Station contained three vertical Gordon Water Turbines driving two 25 KW and one 185 KW Direct Current Generators, and was officially opened in 1913; a battery was installed at Crane Street Works and the surplus energy generated at night by this Power Station was used to charge the batteries which assisted to supply the current required on peak load. This plant was supplemented in 1932 by a motor convertor to convert the Direct Current to three phase Alternating Current to suit the new conditions brought about by the change over from Direct to Alternating Current distribution. The electricity generated averaged 1.25 million units per annum which, at the time the plant was installed, represented over 40% of the total current required to supply the City of Chester, and was generated at a fifth of the cost of the current produced by the Steam Station.[5]

Following the Electricity Act of 1947, which nationalised electricity undertakings, the Hydro-electric Power Station was to be leased to the British Electricity Authority. However, in 1950 the site was taken over by the West Cheshire Water Board for subsequent use as a water pumping station.

References

1. N. Cossons, 'The BP book of Industrial Archaeology', p. 225.
2. Chester City Record Office (C.R.O), Ref. 943- 714-338-762131,
   'City of Chester Electricity Undertaking 1896-1946', (Chester: 1946), p. 12.
3. ibid., p. 23.
4. ibid., p. 12.
5. ibid., p. 12.

Hydro-electric Power Station of 1913
114

Salmon

Fishing

After the Norman conquest, the whole course of the River Dee which lay within the boundaries of the earldom of Chester belonged to the Earl and was entirely under his control. *Neither a net could be thrown or a boat launched without his permission.*1

The Abbot of St. Werburgh, or the Monks of Poulton, needed a special grant from the Earl before they could launch even a common fishing-boat upon the Dee. A deed from Ranulph, 4th Earl of Chester, indicates the importance placed on the river's fishing rights:

*...the tenth penny of all my revenue of the city (Chester), and of every fish in the water of the Dee.*2

King Edward III granted a charter of confirmation of the Dee fishing rights to the Abbot and Monks of Dieu-la-Cresse, near Leek. These monks originally came from Combermere Abbey. They settled at Poulton, near Eaton, where they had a monastery built for them.3 A deed of confirmation from Ranulf, 4th Earl of Chester, gave them the right to put one boat upon the waters of the Dee to fish above and below the bridge:

*...to have one free boat in the waters of Chester, without any impediment for ever, and free and quiet liberty to fish below the Bridge of Chester and above the said Bridge, and elsewhere, wherever there is any fishing, with free boats, with every kind of net, in the water of Dee by day and night, as well at Eaton as elsewhere...*4

The permission to "fish by day and by night" was a very special privilege in those days of feudal tenure and of the curfew. Even as late 1540, in Henry VIII's reign, a law was passed against stealing fish from private ponds, where a distinction was made between the offence being committed by day or night:

*...fishing in private ponds, stews, or motes, with intent to steal pikes, bremes, carpes, and other fishes, by persons of no good rule or honesty, little regarding God, is made punishable with imprisonment: but if the same be committed between the hours of six in the evening and six in the morning, it is made felony and punishable with death.*5

The provisions in Magna Charta relating to matters concerning rivers generally, and the several statutes subsequently passed on the same subject, were ultimately placed under the supervision of a commission called the `Commission of Sewers`, which was still in existence in the reign of James I. The Commission's duties included:

...scrutiny over all the navigable channels, investigation of grievances, abate nuisances, pull down weirs, remove stakes, or, as they were called, "kiddles", obstructing the navigation; to destroy stake nets, and protect the salmon fisheries

*and young fry...and, in fact, to adjudicate in all matters affecting the public welfare as regarded rivers and their fisheries.*6

One important feature in the history of the Dee, at least from the fishery at Eaton to the sea, was its claim of a separate jurisdiction, distinct from that over other British rivers, as belonging to the earls of Chester, and a right to enforce its own peculiar law, which was exercised not only by the earls themselves, but by the descendants of those who held from them, into the 18th century.7

As early as the reign of Edward III, there was a particular office called "The Sergeancy of the Dee", which possessed the exclusive right of proceeding in matters relating to the River Dee.8 At the time of Edward III, Robert de Eton laid claim to the Sergeancy of the Dee. Included in de Eton's claim are interesting details of the methods of catching fish at that time:

*Robert de Eton claims to have for himself and his heirs the Sergeancy of the water of Dee... that is to have custody of the said water, and to 'attach' trespassers fishing in the said water... That is to say, the opening of the current of the water from nets unlawfully placed there to the damage of our Lord Earl; that is with nets placed in the said water which are called "stal-nettes", which exceed the measurement of nine fathoms, and the "dog-rope" of one fathom; and if the stake to which the dog-rope is attached be deeper in the water than to a man's knee, then the said nets remain forfeited... taking and doing from the said pool as far as the stall nets are accustomed to be set; that is, from the Bridge of Dee to the boundaries of 'Blaken'; and from thence, as far as Arnoldshire, the Lord shall have all nets called stall nets, except one which the said Robert shall have, with all the fish, that is which are forfeited, because that a boat of twenty feet long, with oars sixteen feet in length, cannot pass through the middle of the said water without touching the said nets. He claims also for him and his heirs to have, that is to place, stakes and clays (clayas) in the water, where he may fasten and tie his nets and engines for fishing... He claims also for him and his heirs to have two stalls in the said water of the Dee for fishing with four nets, which are called stall nets; and claims also for him and his heirs to have two boats upon the said water to fish with at his pleasure...*9

The main methods of taking fish in early times were by weirs, stake nets and fixed traps (called *ingenia*). There were frequent references to "stall nets" and "stalls in Dee". Stalls appear to have been certain portions of the banks of the river from which a stake net was projected into the water, and were only illegal if exceeding a certain size, or set by persons with no right to fish. That "stalls" and "stall nets" were two distinct things is evident from Robert de Eton's claim of two stalls capable of setting four nets.10

The most important of the "several" fisheries of the Dee were those of the Dee Mills. As late as 1911, a conveyance mentions the remains of a Salmon Cage on the Handbridge end of the weir:

...The said Duke as Beneficial Owner hereby conveys unto the Purchasers

*... that building (now partially pulled down) formerly used as a Salmon Cage situated at the head of the King's Pool on the River Dee near to and on the East side of the Old Dee Bridge...***11**

A fish weir used to serve this salmon cage, which was located *30 yards* below the causeway. No trace of the cage survived, but it was constructed on the principal of allowing fish to enter through the `hecks` or needles which prevented their escape. It worked in the following way; a sluice near to the southern end of the main weir or causeway was opened and water rushed with great force down the race or stream across which the cage was erected. The strong current enticed the salmon, which were then caught in the trap.**12**

The owner of the cage also enjoyed the exclusive right of taking *Salmon Lampreys Eeles and other sorts and kinds of fish* in the King's Pool *with nets and other engines (traps).***13** But the passing of the Fisheries Act of 1861 meant he could not exercise those salmon fishery rights unless water enabled the fish to pass up and down. Now the owner of that fishery did not own the causeway, and to have built such a salmon ladder would have ruined the milling rights at Chester. Consequently, the netting rights and the right of the cage fishery were *for ever forfeited and lost because the fish-pass was not put in and could not be put in by the owner of the fishing rights.***14**

The cage fishery was not specifically mentioned until the middle of the 16th century. However, salmon had been caught hereabouts ever since the causeway was built - if only with stake nets and weirs composed of piles driven into the river bed and wattled to form a fence. In 'Cheshire in the Pipe Rolls, 1158-1301', there is an item: *Revenue appears from the salmon stakes and nets at the Dee Causeway* in 1289.**15** There is also an entry in Vale Royal Abbey's Building Accounts, dated 1277/8, *For driving pales in the weir (chausia) of the water of the Dee 40s.***16** This work was necessary because *such great floods came down... that the fishery 'crates' (wattle hurdles) could not be fixed beneath the bridge,* so that no one *could take fish there except by nets for the greater part of the year; and the fishery weirs (gurgites) were scattered by the floods* for four years in succession.**17**

The sale of fish was strictly regulated by the Chester Assembly:
*At an Assembly held in 25 Hen. VIII by Henry Gee, Mayor, with the Aldermen and Common Council, it was ordered that all fresh fish coming to the city to be sold (such as Salmon, Mylvell, Rey or any other Sea Fish) should be taken to the King's board for sale. No persons should buy fish there before nine o'clock, except citizens for their own households. From nine until ten o'clock the fishmongers should buy. At ten o'clock the foreign fishers should have liberty to cut and retail their fish. Fish coming in boats to be sold in the city should not be sold until the Mayor, by his officers, should see the city served, then the fishmongers and then the country carriers... it was further ordered that the fishmongers of the city and all other persons bringing fish to the market should expose them all to open view and not conceal them upon the like penalty.***18**

In 1748, John Phillips, a carpenter, drowned while making a new salmon cage at the east end of the causeway above the Dee Bridge. Phillips was using a *corrikle* (coracle) to gain access to the site of the salmon cage, and for some strange reason he jumped from this craft, when it was halfway across the river, and attempted to swim to the shore.**19**

Salmon Fishing in the Dee, 1890s   *Courtesy of L Morgan*

By 1880, Fishery Boards were well established and licences were required by the many full-time salmon fisherman. In 1882, a licence to net salmon, valid from April 1, cost £5. The newly-appointed rector of Old St. Mary's, went to see the first day's salmon fishing and saw several men standing around idly because they could not afford the licence money. He decided to help the fishermen raise the licence money by the inception of an award for the first salmon caught at the season's opening.

The rector, a good and practical man, was sympathetic and anxious for the welfare of his fishermen-parishioners. He had the idea of forming a Parish Bank, with contributions as low as one penny, so that the fishermen could save up for the licence fees. He also gave a prize of a ton of coal to the fishermen who landed the first catch of the season and displayed it at the Rectory. Successive rectors have continued this charitable practice, but since the price of coal has gone up disproportionately to the parish stipend, today's award is of token value. Most of the fishermen lived in Greenway Street, which may have been named after Joseph Greenway or his kin, who rented the Salmon Cage from Robert Topham in the 1840s.**20**

Off For A Day`s Fishing From The Duke Of Wellington, 1900 -1905
Courtesy of L Morgan

Fish Pass

In 1896, when the Chester Sluices Bill was under consideration, a large amount of evidence was given with respect to the Fishery interests. Fish requiring to pass up the river apparently waited in the King's Pool, just below the weir (towards the left bank). They got over the weir either when the tide rose above it, or when there was sufficient depth of water from above flowing over the weir. When coming down the river the fish waited above the weir till the tide, or the upland flow over it, gave them an opportunity to pass. It was stated in evidence that, in 1896, owing to the lowness of the water, fish had been waiting above the weir six weeks up to June 23rd of that year to get down. The water was one foot below the crest of the weir on the upstream side.**21**

A movable fish pass, *16 feet wide, of a special and novel design*, was proposed in the (rejected) Sluices Bill, but those who gave evidence on behalf of the Fishery Interest did not approve of the fish pass, as they did not consider it sufficient to compensate for the damaging effect of the sluices in almost completely isolating the upper part of the river, above the weir, from the sea. **22**

In 1911 and 1912, Hugh Edmund Ethelston Peel and Sir Henry Beyer Robertson, who were leading players on behalf of the Fisheries interests, took control of the south bank of the King's Pool. Both these men were owners of important fisheries in the River Dee and were stated as:

*having the interests of the Fisheries of the River at heart.***23**

In 1911, Peel and Robertson purchased the Salmon Cage and eastern part of the Causeway for £10, together with the Handbridge Mills for £140, from the Duke of Westminster:

First all those buildings hereditaments and premises with the fixed machinery therein ... forming the Water Mill on the South side of the Causeway on the River Dee ... commonly known as "The Snuff Mill" formerly in the occupation of William Catlewgh Jones and afterwards of Messieurs Nicholls ... Secondly all that Manufactory or Mill now or heretofore used as a Watermill and called "The Old Mill" jutting into the River Dee and situate at Handbridge ... at the Eastern end of the Causeway running between the said Mill and the Old Dee Mills (or the site thereof) at the Western end of such Causeway formerly in the occupation of Mrs. Harriot Holley ... And in particular a right of way road or passage for all purposes ... and at all times ... leading from Handbridge aforesaid and known as Mill Street and Tophams Lane... Thirdly all that Manufactory or Mill now or heretofor used as a Water Mill and called "The New Mill" situate on the left Bank of the River Dee at Handbridge ... formerly in the occupation of Edward Jones and Sons Tobacco Manufacturers ... Subject ... the said hereditaments should not at any time thereafter be used as a Mill for grinding Wheat Rye Barley or other kind of grain .. Fourthly all that building (now partially pulled down) formerly used as a Salmon Cage near to and on the East side of The Old Dee Bridge ...Together with the Stone Causeway adjoining such Salmon Cage on the North side thereof and jutting out into the said King's Pool And also the Stone Walls or abutements on the South side of the said Salmon Cage... **24**

Peel and Robertson issued a directive that on their deaths the *Salmon Cage, Causeway and Mills* in Handbridge should be offered for sale to the Conservators of the River Dee Fishery District who:

shall be at liberty to purchase the same at a price equal to the money which we or either of us have expended in such purchase... **25**

In 1912, Peel and Robertson purchased the sites of Tophams Lane, Mill Street, other rights of way and parts of the King's Pool river bank from Robert Topham and others. **26**

In 1911, A.C. Hurtzig issued a report on S.E.Britton's scheme for an Hydro-electric Power Station on the site of the Old Dee Mills (on the bridge). Hurtzig had no objection to the construction of a fish pass and concluded, with respect to the Dee fisheries, that:

I have no objection to a fish pass, and its provision will, at all events, keep the upper and lower compartments of the river in continuous communication for fish. The other conditions of the upper compartment of the river when the new Power Scheme is realised will, in this connection, be less disadvantageous than they were when the "Old Dee Mills" were in operation, and the depth above the Weir will never be drawn down so low as it frequently was in those days. Generally speaking, therefore, and from the above points of view, I should say that the Authorities in charge of the Fishery Interests cannot but be satisfied with the proposals of the Scheme. **27**

The Building of the Hydro-electric Power Station started in 1911 and was completed in 1913. The same year, a deed of covenant was made between Chester Corporation, the River Dee Fisheries Board and Peel/Robertson, which laid down strict conditions on the extraction of water for the generation of electricity:

*... the Fishery Board consider it of great importance that for the maintenance of the stock of Salmon in the River [Dee] there should be as little diminution as possible in the quantity of water which should pass over the Weir at all times of the year for the purpose of enabling fish to ascend the River...*28

It was agreed that the Council would pay the Fishery Board £500 for work for the *improvement and in the interests of the Fisheries.* This work included the construction of a *Fish Pass* in the neighbourhood of the Weir. In order to keep the river water at an acceptable level above the Weir, it was agreed that a continuous flow of water of *750 cubic feet per minute* be maintained over the Weir. If the Council used a greater quantity than *61,000 cubic feet of water per minute*, then the Fishery were entitled to increase the flow of water *above 750 cubic feet per minute* by a specified amount.29

It was also agreed that during the months of; March, April, May and June in each year (but not exceeding in the whole nine weeks in any such year) when the young salmon came down the River Dee on their journey to the sea, that Chester Council would fit a grating or strainer over the sluices to the hydroelectric works, fitted with an agreed size of mesh, for that period.30 In addition to the above clauses, the 1913 covenant also placed many technical requirements and response times on Chester City Council.

However, the River Dee Fishery Board Annual Report for 1914 stated that the turbines of the hydroelectric works had adverse effects on the Fishery:

*"In the Spring of 1914, Fry going down the river collected in vast numbers in the head race of the Works and were considerably delayed in getting out to sea... Great apprehension was felt as to their safety, as some Fry were going through the gratings... Water Bailiffs and fishermen kept look-out during the time fish were going down [river] but only one [fish] was found dead in the Chester District... During April, May and June large quantities of salmon were seen in the tail race of the Works 'Having been enticed there by a great volume of water passing through the turbines... Damage occurs when the turbines have stopped and salmon go in and are caught when they (turbines) start to revolve again...*31

Nevertheless, all the news, in 1914 was not bad. The new fish pass at Chester was in *excellent repair* and had withstood the *recent* heavy floods and was working satisfactorily.32 In 1915, the Fisheries continued to record major problems with the hydroelectric works, and Chester Council agreed to increase the flow of water over the weir from *750 to 1,000 cubic feet per minute*. Also, the level of water below which the Council could not draw off water from the River Dee was raised from *13.75 to 15.65 above Ordnance Datum*, as fixed by the bench mark on the Bridge Gate.33

The year 1916 was remarkable for the salmon netsmen, when 24 salmon were taken in one "draft", at a market value of £25. In those years, it was not uncommon for 17 to 20 salmon or more to be taken in a single draft. Most of these fish were taken in the vicinity of Handbridge, and were of uniform size and high quality. It was stated that the fish were:

*Undoubtedly fish which had dropped down the river from the tail race of the Hydro Electricity Works, where they congregated.*34

During the summer months of 1916, great shoals of porpoises frequented the river and estuary, and at times practically stopped the run of fish up the river. Many salmon were caught which were badly maimed by the porpoises. It was commented that there seemed to be no effective way of dealing with *these pests*. Early in March 1916, several otters were seen in the tail race of the Hydro-electric Power Station, and a female weighing 10 lbs. was caught.35

In the latter part of 1916, Chester Corporation, under protest from the Fisheries Board, obtained power under the Defence of the Realm Act. to put a temporary concrete curb on the Chester Weir 12" (0.3 metres) in height and raise the level of the controlling stop of the fish pass. This work was carried out in October 1916. Consequently, the water in the river was kept at a one foot higher level, which created a greater flow of water through the turbines at the electricity works. The tail race of the works had, in consequence, a much greater volume of water and attracted large numbers of salmon. Large numbers of these salmon were caught by the net fishermen who worked in the vicinity of Greenway Street, Handbridge. The Fisheries complained that these fish were *lost to the Fisheries* and that something should be done to prevent the fish from getting into the tail race.36

In 1917, 1,000 salmon were caught in one week's fishing below the weir. The heaviest fish caught weighed *42lbs*.37 The Fisheries Board complained that the capture of so many fish below Chester Weir was to be *deplored*, and that the raising of the weir stopped fish reaching their spawning ground. Another obstruction that the Board complained about was the tail race of the hydro-works, which attracted the fish away from the weir and held them up until high tide, when they would fall back with the ebb and were caught by the net fishermen. The Board complained that *The outlook for the coming seasons is not promising*.38 Also, the fish pass had been increased in height and was causing a problem. The Fisheries Board alleged that the increased height kept out many tides and also held-up floods and freshets (rushes of fresh water flowing into the sea; floods of river from rain or melted snow.) in the upper river - which were quickly drawn off by the hydro-works to below the sill of the weir, so that water ran over the curb for a very short period during the time of abnormal floods and tides of *20 feet and over*. Since the erection of the Hydro-Works the Weir had been raised *thrice* to an extent of *one foot 11 inches*, and kept the *King's Pool stagnant*.39

In 1918, thousands of smolt and hundreds of kelt were held-up in front of the gratings of the *Hydro*. Porpoises were again causing trouble and a drought was recorded.40 In

1922, The Fisheries Report started with the brusque statement that *The River Dee is suffering from abstraction of water*, for use by both the towns of Warrington and Birkenhead.**41** It was reported that Chester Council had finally removed the kerb from the weir.**42**

The 1920s were generally good years for salmon fishing, with the exception of 1929, which was a very bad season. There was a very cold winter, followed by severe drought and then flooding. The river burst its banks and not within *living memory* had such extremes been seen. Even so, considering the conditions the Dee netsmen had a good season, with good market prices for the salmon.**43**

The year 1925 is significant, because of the absence of any reference to problems caused by the hydro-works. In 1926, the market price of salmon fell, which was alleged to be caused by so many large catches and by the *new methods* of preserving fish, which allowed imported fish to be sold in the markets of Britain.**44**

In 1928, a sturgeon, 136 kg in weight and 2.48m long, was caught by Joseph Johnson and Thomas Totty:

*The type of sea monster which had for a few days in mid-August exercised the minds of Dee fishermen and occasioned a good deal of perturbation and speculation was definitely settled on the evening of 14 Aug. when Mr. Joseph Johnson, senior, and Mr. Thomas Totty, junior, both of Greenway Street, fishing with their net in the stretch of water between the Grosvenor Road bridge and the railway bridge, Chester, landed a royal sturgeon. The big fish made a gallant fight for liberty and tore the net literally to pieces in the struggle. Eventually, with the aid of half-a-dozen other fishermen, Mr. Johnson landed his catch, killed the fish and passed it over to the care of a local fishmonger, Mr. T.E. Hughes, of Brook Street. The fishermen were previously concerned as to whether the fish was a whale, shark or porpoise... Mr. Joseph Johnson said he and Totty were fishing for salmon with their net on Friday evening. They knew that some big fish had been in the water all the week, and only the previous evening a hole of considerable size had been made in their net. Asked how he landed the sturgeon, Mr. Johnson said, "We got him (actually, it was a female) in the best way we could and by letting him do as he liked... I was proud to land him... It was the sight of a lifetime to see him in the water..".***45**

Mr Hughes was not sure of the proper procedure to sell the sturgeon, because these fish belong to the Crown. He made enquiries and received a *communication* from the Board of Trade. The board informed him that all sturgeon caught within territorial waters were Fishes Royal and belonged to the Crown, except where the right to such fish has been granted in favour of other parties. Fishes Royal also included porpoises, dolphins and whales. The correct procedure was to report the capture of a sturgeon to the local Receiver of Wrecks (the collector of Customs and Excise at Chester). The proceeds of the sale of the sturgeon were to be forwarded to the Receiver, together with the name of its captor. Mr Hughes ran a competition, in aid of the Royal Infirmary, at guessing the sturgeon's weight and the most accurate received a prize.

Sadly, owing to the warm weather, the fish was unfit to eat when authority was given to dispose of it. Thus nearly 7 kilo of caviar were wasted.**46** Over the years, several sturgeon have been caught in the River Dee, though normally not as large as the above fish and not so far upriver. There is a preserved sturgeon, approximately two metres long, in the Grosvenor Museum's Natural History Collection.

Drying The Salmon Nets At `Nowhere` During High Tide, 1950
Courtesy of L Morgan

In 1950, the Hydro-electric Power Station closed. With the exception of the years 1952 and 1959, the 1950s were comparatively poor years for catches of salmon. However, 1966 was described as *the best season since 1939... with an upward trend since the doldrums of 1953-56.***47** Since the 1970s, there has been a general decline in the crop of salmon caught. However, in 1994, while the number of salmon reaching Chester Weir was not the highest recorded, the declared net catch was the best of the decade at 1,470 fish.**48**

The Dee Stock Assessment Programme

In 1989, the Welsh Region of the National Rivers Authority, now the Environment Agency, began an exciting research programme into the salmon and sea trout of the River Dee. This study (DSAP) combines some important new initiatives with several existing approaches to form an integrated study of the river-based life stages. In broad terms, the study aims to obtain better measures of both the numbers of fish entering the river each year and the factors which influence them - whether man-induced (e.g. effects of the rod and net fisheries, pollution, stocking) or otherwise (environmental effects). Improving the understanding of the salmon and sea trout resources in this way leads to more effective management - benefiting both fish and fishermen alike.**49**

Spring 1991 saw the launch of two new investigations to complete the present phase of the DSAP: a) Adult tagging and recapture study and Chester Weir fish trap and b) Radiotracking programme.

a) The Adult tagging and recapture study and Chester Weir fish trap study relies on rod and net fishermen to report any tagged salmon or sea trout they capture and these returns, when compared with catches of untagged fish, allow estimates to be made of the number of fish entering the river each season. Essential to this exercise, apart from the co-operation of the fishermen, is the use of a permanent fish trap at Chester Weir where fish are caught and tagged. Improvements to the Chester Weir site were made in 1990-91, including extension of the old 'counter' building over the trap channel, and the incorporation of penstock sluices at each end of the channel to shut off the flow when the trap is being checked. The modified structure provides a safe and secure facility geared towards making the whole capture and tagging process as stress free for the fish as possible.

The fish are tagged with small coloured plastic tags known as Floy tags. These are harmlessly inserted just below the dorsal fin while the fish is anaesthetised, and are visible on the outside of the body. Each tag bears a unique number, the NRA (now Environment Agency) address and a reward statement offering £5 for each tag returned. In addition to supplying fish for tagging, the trap is useful in a number of other ways including; I) yielding biological information (e.g. length, weight, sex) essential to other aspects of the DSAP. II) acting as a sampling device for microtag returns - supplementing data from the fisheries, and III) providing an indicator of the size of the run based on catch alone.**50**

b) In the Radiotracking programme, special tags are used which emit a radio or acoustic signal and allow the movements of individual salmon and sea trout to be followed from the estuary to the spawning tributaries. The technique will reveal a great deal about the factors which affect fish movements (e.g. flow water quality, physical barriers including Chester Weir and trap) and how fish interact with the fisheries. If captured by fishermen, radiotagged fish appear no different from the trap tagged fish - carrying the same type of Floy tag although the tag colour and wording are different. However, a £25 reward is offered for radiotagged fish, £5 for the Floy tag and a further £20 for the radio tag. The latter rests in the stomach and can be reused.**51**

So the Dee study represents a unique approach, which Fisheries scientists believe will not only improve their knowledge and management of the salmon and sea trout resource on the Dee, but will help to learn lessons which can be applied to fisheries both nationally and internationally.**52**

Byelaws

In 1996, the Environment Agency proposed a new Net Limitation Order and Net Fishing Byelaws for the River Dee, which are in the process of ratification, to protect the salmon of the River Dee. The Environment Agency found that the net catch of salmon has shown an overall decline since the mid to late 1970s, although this has stabilised to around 1,000 fish in recent years. This decline is mainly attributed to the draft net catch with the trammel net catch being remarkably stable. Salmon catch per tide by both methods show an apparent increasing trend in recent years. The average catch per licence is around 36 salmon each year for draft nets and 82 salmon per year for trammel nets. There has been full licence uptake of the four available trammel net licences sine 1985, whereas full uptake of the available 30 draft net licences has not occurred since 1986, with an average uptake of 16 licences over the last five years.

Radio tracking studies have shown that about 1 in 3 salmon are displaced at least once for distances in excess of one km from Chester Weir. Displaced fish represent a significant proportion (35%) of draft catches at the two netting stations closet to the weir. The available evidence indicates that salmon egg deposition on the Dee has fallen below acceptable levels in recent years and therefore measures are required to help increase spawning escapement.

The Environment Agency's proposals are that the number of draft nets should be reduced to 16, and trammel nets to two under a reducing Net Limitation Order (NLO). In order to ensure that wide distribution of the draft nets takes place, in relation to the number of available netting stations, the Agency recommends that they should be segregated to the following areas and allocated accordingly: Chester to Queensferry Bridge - 8 nets, and Queensferry Bridge downstream - 8 nets. The Agency also propose that a Byelaw should be promoted to extend the prohibited area for netting downstream to a line drawn across the River Dee at Cop Point. This will protect fish which drop back from Chester Weir preventing excessive exploitation in this reach and thus serving as a significant stock conservation measure.53

The Environment Agency say that the major effect of the proposed Order will be to reduce the maximum number of nets operating from 30 to 16 draft nets and 4 to 2 trammel nets. The present licencees, who have held a licence for the previous two years and who are dependent on fishing for their livelihood, are protected under the provisions of the proposed Order. They will be able to continue fishing until they decide to retire or leave the fishery for some reason. However, no new draft or trammel net licences would be allowed to enter the fishery until the number of existing licences falls below 16 and 2 respectively. The proposed reduction in nets will result in an annual saving of salmon. This could amount to an estimated 115 fish annually. A proportion of these fish will be taken by rods (18%), or will subsequently die from other causes (8%), leaving average of 87 fish to spawn and contribute 250,000 eggs.

The Agency expect that greater and more immediate fish savings can be expected from the introduction of the proposed byelaw. Radio tracking studies (DSAP) from 1991-93, indicated that 31% of salmon reaching Chester Weir subsequently dropped back into the net fishery. Of these fish, around 50% were caught by draft nets operating upstream of Cop point, with the remainder crossing the weir at a later date. This amounts to an escapement of fish reaching Chester Weir, principally in July and August, of about 80% and is equivalent to an average run size at this time of year of 2,350 salmon. Consequently, an estimated 569 fish would have dropped back from the weir and been caught by the Chester drafts. Introduction of the byelaw will help to conserve these fish, leaving an average of 442 to spawn. The combination of the proposed NLO and byelaw changes could, in time, ensure the deposition of an additional 1.5 million eggs above the resulting stock levels and make a significant contribution to the short fall identified from spawning targets.

The 1996 proposals are in addition to byelaws passed in 1995, when in order to protect diminishing spring salmon stocks, the start of the netting season was put back from the 1st March to 1st May.[54]

References

1.   W. Ayrton, Records relating to the River Dee, and its Fisheries, 'Journal of the Chester Archaeological Society', 6, 1849-55, p. 234.
2.   ibid., p. 235.
3.   ibid., p. 236.
4.   ibid., p. 237.
5.   ibid., p. 237.
6.   ibid., p. 239.
7.   ibid., p. 239.
8.   ibid., p. 239.
9.   ibid., pp. 240-241.
10. ibid., p. 245.
11. Birch Cullimore & Co., (Solicitors) Chester, 'Conveyance of a Salmon Cage, Causeway and Mills on the River Dee in the City of Chester', 12th May 1911, p. 3.
12. 'Chester Chronicle', 29 Sept. 1866, p. 6.
13. Chester City Record Office (C.R.O.), CHD/13/16.
14. 'Chester Chronicle', 25 March 1916, p. 6.
15. 'Cheshire in the Pipe Rolls', 1158-1301, 'The Record Society of Lancashire and Cheshire' (R.S.L.C.) Vol 92 (1938), p. 92.
16. 'Ledger Book of Vale Royal Abbey', in R.S.L.C., Vol 68 (1913), p. 195.
17. Calender of County Court, City Court and Eyre Rolls of Chester, 1259-97, 'Cheetham Society', Vol 84 (1925), p. 151.
18. Chester City Record Officer, Assembly Book, AF/10, 8 July 1701, p. 100.
19. Chester City Record Office, `Coroner's Inquests`, QCI/21/27. Sep 17th 1748, Death of John Phillips
20. Chester Public Library, 'Studies in Local History No. 5, Handbridge',   G.R.Coppack, 'A Handbridge Miscellany' (Chester: 1964), p. 29.
21. "Dee Mills Water Power Scheme", 'Report by Mr. A. C. Hurtzig on Mr. S. E. Brittain's Scheme for Generating Electricity from Water Power at the Weir, Chester' (London: 1911), p. 8.
22. ibid., p. 8.

23. Henry Jollife (Solicitor), Chester, Deed of Convenant Between - Chester City Council and the River Dee Fisheries, 'As to the execution of certain Works and the control of the River water at or near the Weir across the River Dee in the City of Chester', Dated 5th April 1913, p. 2.

24. Birch Cullimore (Solicitor), 'Conveyance of a Salmon Cage, Causeway and Mills on the River Dee in the City of Chester', from The Duke of Westminster to Hugh. E. E. Peel, and Sir Henry B. Robertson, Dated 12th May 1911, pp. 1-3.

25. ibid., unnumbered.

26. 'Conveyance of the sites of Tophams Lane, Mill Street and other certain rights of way at Handbridge in the City of Chester', From Robert Topham and others to H.E.E. Peel and Sir H.B. Robertson, Dated 24th July 1912, p. 1.

27. 'Dee Mills Water Power Scheme' by A.C. Hurtzig, p. 8.

28. Deed of Covenant, 'As to the Execution of certain Works and the Control of River Water', Dated 5th April 1913, p. 2.

29. ibid., p. 5.

30. ibid., p. 8.

31. Environment Agency (E.A.), Buckley, 'The River Dee Fishery Board Annual Report' for 1910, p. 10.

32. ibid., p. 10.

33. Henry Jollife, Chester (Solicitor), Deed of Covenant Between - Chester City Council and the Fisheries Board, dated 17th July 1915, pp. 1-4.

34. E.A., 'Dee Fisheries Board Report', 1916, p. 9.

35. ibid., p. 10.

36. ibid., p. 11.

37. ibid., 1917, pp. 8-9.

38. ibid., 1917, p. 9.

39. ibid., 1917, p. 11.

40. ibid., 1918, pp. 9-15.

41. ibid., 1921, pp. 10-13.

42. ibid., 1922, pp. 9-12.

43. ibid., 1929. pp. 8-10.

44. E.A., 'Dee Fisheries Report', 1926, p. 10.

45. Chester Military Museum (C.M.M.), 'The Oak Leaf', Regimental Journal, October 1928 (With acknowledgments to 'The Chester Observer', 25 Aug.1928) pp. 454-456.

46. ibid., pp. 454-456.

47. E.A., 'Dee & Clwyd River Authority Report' for 1966, p. 8.

48. I.C. Davidson, R.J. Cove & N.J. Milner, 'Dee Stock Assessment Programme - Annual Report for 1994' (Environment Agency: Cardiff, 1996), p. 46.

49. National Rivers Authority (NRA) - Welsh Region, 'Salmon and Sea Trout Studies on the River Dee', information leaflet (Mold: NRA, c.1992), p. 2.

50. ibid., p. 4.

51. ibid., pp. 5-6.

52. ibid., p. 6.

53. Environment Agency (E.A.) Welsh Region, Alan Winston, 'Net Limitation Order and Net Fishing Byelaw for the River Dee', Summary Proof of Evidence, October 1996, Section 10 - Conclusions and Recommendations.

54. ibid., Section 11 - Benefits of the Proposed Order and Net Byelaw Amendment.

A Salmon

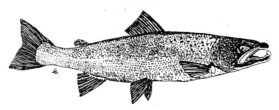